Emperor's Spear

Alex Gough is an author of Roman historical adventures. The Carbo Chronicles, including *Watchmen of Rome* and *Bandits of Rome*, was written as a result of a lifelong obsession with ancient Rome, and the culmination of a lot of research into the underclasses of the time. He has also written a collection of adventures following Carbo and other characters from *Watchmen of Rome*, where you can learn more about their rich lives.

For reviews of Roman fiction, and articles about Roman history go to www.romanfiction.com

Also by Alex Gough

*Carbo and the Thief
Who All Die*

Carbo of Rome

*Watchmen of Rome
Bandits of Rome*

The Imperial Assassin

*Emperor's Sword
Emperor's Knife
Emperor's Axe
Emperor's Spear*

ALEX GOUGH
EMPEROR'S
SPEAR

CANELO

First published in the United Kingdom in 2021 by

Canelo
31 Helen Road
Oxford OX2 0DF
United Kingdom

A CIP catalogue record for this book is available from the British Library.

Print ISBN 978 1 80032 216 5
Ebook ISBN 978 1 80032 212 7

Look for more great books at www.canelo.co

Printed and bound in Great Britain by Clays Ltd, Elcograf S.p.A.

Chapter One

Martius 213 AD

On the peaceful island of Lipari, with the gulls keowing loudly as they circled over the waves crashing against the cliffs, a gentle sea breeze washing the villa in clean scents, the sun warming all beneath it benignly, Silus carefully set down his cup of exquisite Falernian and said, 'Fuck.'

Oclatinius simply nodded, giving it a moment to sink in.

Silus had known it was going to be a bad day as soon as he had seen the boat come into view over the horizon. It was a fast liburnian bireme, the type used by the Roman navy as escorts, scouts and pirate hunters. And sometimes as a means of transporting someone important quickly and safely.

When he had recognised Oclatinius disembarking, he had known for certain it was going to be bad news.

But not this bad.

'When?' he asked, eventually.

'A few weeks ago.'

'Weeks! Why wasn't I told sooner?'

'Germania is a long way away. It was some time before anyone even knew he was in trouble. Then the report had to be relayed to Festus and myself. We had to consult the Emperor. And then I had to come here, all the way to the end of the Italian peninsula, to collect your sorry arse and put it back to work.'

Silus simmered, understanding, but not happy about it. Atius. You fucking idiot. And with the anger came guilt. He should never have let him leave on his own. He should never have let his friend go back into the field without Silus there to look out for him, protect him.

But Atius had left, chafing with boredom, while Silus had rested in semi-retirement on this beautiful island, playing at being a surrogate father to Tituria, walking along the cliffs or the beach, even reading sometimes. He had ignored all the supplications and commands to return to duty, and until now, Oclatinius had clearly not felt like pushing the matter.

And now Oclatinius had come to him with a mission the old man knew he could not turn down. The bastard. He was probably delighted that he had found something to drag Silus back into his network of spies, scouts, informants and assassins.

The Arcani.

Silus had known it was too good to last. Since the loss of his family in Britannia, all that time ago, he had been wrestling with intense emotions: grief; anger; desperation; terror. It had all taken its toll.

After he had reunited the young Avitus with his father, Marcellus, he had been required to accompany them to Numidia, to help him carry out the mission for which he had originally been dispatched from Rome to put down the incipient revolt brewing there. And yet this final mission had been almost anti-climactic. They had sailed in with a vexillation of a thousand legionaries and auxiliaries and five hundred cavalry, drawn from the forces stationed in Egypt such as the II Triana, and had marched straight to the governor's palace.

Although they had been considerably delayed on their journey to Numidia by the kidnapping of Marcellus' son, they still arrived in the province before the governor, Quintus Cornelius Valens, had had time to advance his plans of rebellion to any sufficient degree. Silus had thought the situation could have been more dangerous. After all, Septimius Severus, the current Emperor's father, had started his rebellion from north Africa.

But the III Augusta stationed in Numidia had not been sufficiently persuaded at that stage to join Valens in revolt. Maybe they were loyal to Caracalla, who was always popular with the common soldier, or maybe they had not been offered a sufficiently large bribe and were holding out for a better offer. Whatever the case, when Marcellus arrived with his show of force, the III Augusta had put up no resistance, and when he had arrested Valens, they had acknowledged Marcellus as the new governor without hesitation.

Of course, it had been Silus' job to execute Valens. Quietly, out of sight. Caracalla hadn't wanted any knowledge of the disloyalty to get out, in case it encouraged others at this fragile moment in his principate.

So Silus had strangled him in his cell. Held a tight cord around the man's neck while he tried to draw in air, while he gripped at the ligature, fingernails gouging bloody streaks into his skin, legs kicking, until after an eternity, his struggles weakened, slowed, stopped.

Silus had thrown the body to the floor, panting, and felt an irrational anger at the dead man. He didn't want to feel like this any more, to do this any more. The fear and anger and guilt and anxiety as he forced the life out of another human. He was done.

And so he had turned his back, and returned to Lipari, where Tituria waited in exile. The young girl, slowly growing up, who hated him as the murderer of her father, and loved him as the man who had saved her life, as the only person left in the world who cared about her.

It was a complicated relationship, but it had grown over the next few months. Not once did Silus miss the action or the adventure of his time in the Arcani, or even his job as a scout with the auxiliaries in northern Britannia. Although of course he missed his late wife and daughter profoundly, he didn't particularly miss the land of his birth. He had everything he needed on Lipari.

Atius had quickly tracked him down, come to find him to make sure his closest friend was well. He had stayed for some time, tired too, and wrestling with confusion about his faith and his place in the world. Lipari was a wonderful place to sit and think, and Atius had done plenty of that. Ultimately, though, the big Celtiberian was too much a man of action to stay long kicking his heels on a remote island. One day, he had announced that he was rejoining the Arcani. Not that either of them had ever officially left. But he had made up his mind. He was going back to Rome, to report to Oclatinius, to take on whatever was asked of him.

Silus had begged him to stay. Atius had begged Silus to go with him. They had exchanged angry words, then apologies, then an embrace, and parted ways. Watching his friend sail away had left Silus more lonely than ever. But though he had brooded for days, Tituria's cheerful and intelligent company, and the affection of Issa, Silus' little old dog that he had gifted to Tituria, had brought him

4

out of his depression. He had settled into a calm routine, until he found that he was happier than at any time since he had lost his family.

And now Oclatinius had pricked that bubble of contentment, and all the joy and peace it had contained had dissipated into the atmosphere.

Atius, you complete arse, Silus thought, then immediately felt guilty at the fact that his friend's plight had engendered pity only for himself. He sighed, picked up his cup of wine, and took a long swallow. It didn't taste nearly as sweet as it had yesterday.

'Tell me everything,' he said.

Januarius 213 AD

Atius really hated snow. He had grown up in Hispania, with its warm climate, and though he had seen plenty of it in his time serving with the auxiliaries in the north of Britannia, he had never formed any sort of rapprochement with the horrible cold stuff. It made marching difficult, it left tracks that an enemy could follow, it was hard to hide against the stark whiteness, it made your fingers clumsy and your toes burn in agony.

And here he was, trekking through forest, beyond the borders of Roman Germania, with an ankle-deep layering of powder impeding him. The snow blustered around him, fortunately covering their tracks soon after they were made. His mind wandered off to Silus. He missed his friend, but sitting around doing nothing on that island had seemed like some kind of hell. Right now, though, the memory was heaven.

He looked back at the men following him. They watched their feet, cursing when they sank too deep, grabbing onto trunks and branches to steady themselves, or haul themselves out of a drift. None looked too pleased to be there, although Memnon, the Aethiopian, seemed to be having the worst of it, born into a country even hotter than Atius' childhood home.

They would need to make camp for the night before too long. Travelling like this was fatiguing, and they also had to think about the plummeting temperature when night fell. He looked toward Aldric, their German guide, who was leading them slowly northwards, then heard a cry from behind him, followed by laughter.

He turned to see the wiry figure of Scaurus flailing around in a deep snowdrift he had fallen head first into. Rather than help him, the other members of his little squad – Toutorix the Gaul, Drustan the Briton and Memnon – all held their sides and guffawed loudly. Scaurus staggered to his feet, spitting and wiping the powder from his eyes and beard. He was coated from head to toe, so he looked like one of the men of snow that the children in the vicus in Britannia used to build in the winter.

Atius found himself smiling like the others, but a glare from Scaurus made him straighten his face. Atius was much bigger than Scaurus, though not as big as Toutorix, who was almost a giant. Nevertheless, there was something about the tough little Roman that was intimidating, even for a grizzled old veteran like himself. It was something mad about the eyes, a wild look that suggested there was something dangerous within, and he was in a constant struggle to keep it safely caged up.

Scaurus turned that gaze on each of the squad, whose faces dropped one by one, turning away as if they had found something fascinating on a branch or under their fingernails. Atius dragged his way over to Scaurus, and roughly brushed away the snow from his shoulders and cloak, ignoring the smaller man's glare.

Eustachys, the tall, thin Greek who marched directly behind Atius, pulled his cloak tighter around himself. Despite being unarmed, and carrying a much less weighty backpack than the rest of the group, he looked the most miserable of them all.

'Could we continue?' he asked through chattering teeth.

Atius gave him a narrow stare, then turned to his men.

'Let's get moving. I want us to find somewhere suitable to camp in the next hour, before it gets too dark and cold.'

The squad set off again. Aldric led the way, glancing up through the coniferous canopy, attempting to catch glimpses of the setting sun through the patchy cloud cover to orient himself. He supplemented his navigational aids with inspection of the moss on the tree trunks and the direction of bend of the scrubby undergrowth protruding up through the snow. Atius stepped in the footprints of the guide, making it easier to walk, and the other squad members did the same in single file behind him. He was aware that they weren't being as cautious as usual, given they were in enemy territory, but sound carried a long way in these cold weather conditions. He was also reassured that they had seen no human footprints in the snow, just those of cloven-hooved animals and birds.

He shouldn't even be here, he reflected with irritation. This mission was supposed to have been led by an experienced member of the speculatores. But the stupid arse had broken a leg during an unofficial horse race, and was laid up for at least two months. That is, if it set straight enough for him to ever walk again. Atius had some sympathy for the poor fellow. It was the sort of foolish piece of showing off he might have done himself until recently. But he had become a more serious, responsible person since his time in Alexandria, and his meetings with the Christian leader Origen. At least, he thought so. It was still all rather confusing.

Regardless of fault, he had been summoned by Oclatinius what seemed like an age ago but had in fact only been a week, and told he was being seconded to work with Festus. This had jarred on so many levels. He liked working for Oclatinius and trusted Festus as far as he could spit a German. Also, this new mission meant pulling him off what he had been working on with Oclatinius, namely the intelligence surrounding Caracalla's expedition to Germania. Long before Caracalla had marched from Rome, Atius and Oclatinius had been in the border province, gathering information and making plans. And finally, although Atius knew he didn't have Silus' cunning and wits, he liked to think he had proven himself enough over the last couple of years to have earned his recent promotion to centurion, and to have his opinions and advice taken seriously. Yet this current mission seemed like a backward step, not worthy of one of the Arcani, but easily undertaken by one of the speculatores or exploratores.

Oclatinius, though, had impressed on Atius the importance of the task. He was to set off with a guide and a small detachment of hand-picked soldiers, to escort Eustachys on an important and highly secret diplomatic mission into Germania Magna, beyond the borders of the Roman provinces. The details of the mission given to Atius were vague, but he knew he had to escort this diplomat who worked for Festus to a rendezvous where he could meet an important nobleman of the Chatti tribe. What he would do in this meeting, Atius could only speculate, but he suspected it would involve attempting to initiate some backstabbing and betrayal within the German confederations. There was always some disenchanted noble with a grudge that could be persuaded to turn traitor.

But before that could take place, Atius had to get this deskbound civilian deep into German territory. And they had to fight through the landscape and the elements, while staying safe from the hostile locals, to get there.

They trudged on predominantly in silence for the next hour, single file behind Aldric, until Atius judged the light was falling to a level that made it sensible to stop for the night. There was no point ploughing on in the gloom, and having someone break an ankle. Although the mission was important, he hadn't been told it was urgent. It was paramount to arrive safely rather than quickly.

They found a small clearing. Although the snow covered most of the signs of human activity, some tree stumps protruded through the white, rough-hewn with an axe, for fuel or building materials. No new twiglets were sprouting, suggesting that they had been cut down within the last few months. But there was no evidence that any locals were still working in the area. Toutorix and Drustan scouted a perimeter around the clearing, and returned to give the all clear. With that, they set their packs down and began to set up camp.

They weren't a legion on the march. There would be no trenches, no palissade. Instead, they trampled down a circle in the snow and laid out their two-man tents in a circle. Memnon found some stones to make a small round hearth, and Scaurus and Aldric gathered some kindling and branches. Eustachys sat on his pack, blowing into his hands and cursing under his breath.

It went against Atius' training and experience to light a fire when sneaking through enemy territory, but he judged that the risk of dying from the cold overnight outweighed the risk of being caught in this desolate and endless forest. Once the fire was lit, a large cooking pot was produced, and Drustan melted some snow in it, then added some dried meat and vegetables. Soon the smell of a decent stew was drifting around the camp, making their mouths water and their stomachs cramp with hunger.

When it was ready, they scooped the stew into their bronze pots and ate hungrily, consuming it as hot as they could without scalding their mouths. Atius took first watch, like a good leader, setting an example, though his belly threatened to rebel. Marching in the cold seemed to provoke a hunger you just didn't feel in warmer weather.

When the others had eaten, Toutorix relieved him, and he sat next to Eustachys, sighing at the twin pleasures of taking the weight off his feet and basking in the warmth of the fire on his face. He filled his bowl and ate, wriggling his toes to try to relieve the needle stabs that accompanied the returning blood flow.

For a while they sat in silence, regaining strength and heat as the darkness fell. The only sounds were the wind rustling the branches of the trees, the crackle of the fire, and the crunch of Toutorix's footsteps as he patrolled in a circle around them.

'Stew was good,' said Atius.

'Very good,' said Memnon, voice deep and husky.

'Yes,' said Aldric.

'Good enough for Jupiter Optimus Maximus,' said Scaurus.

They all turned to look at Eustachys, who was staring at the fire, his hands pressed between his knees, shivering. He looked up.

'Too thin,' he said, and looked back down again.

Drustan frowned at this slight on his cooking, and the others looked offended on his behalf, but Eustachys ignored them, lost in his own misery.

'What a job,' said Scaurus bitterly. 'Babysitting a puny Greek flower.'

The others muttered agreement, and though Atius felt the same, he felt obliged to speak up on behalf of their charge.

'Eustachys isn't trained like we are. He's going through physical hardship he has never had to endure before.'

'Because he is woman,' said Memnon, and the others laughed at the witticism.

'My cock is twice the size of yours,' said Eustachys, summoning some defiance and attempting to match the soldiers for vulgarity.

'Shame it has only been up your boss's arse then,' said Scaurus, drawing another round of laughter.

'Enough,' said Atius, suppressing his own smile. 'Leave the poor man alone. He has a job to do that's vital for Rome, and it is up to us to keep him safe so he can do it.'

'Fuck Rome,' said Drustan, 'shoving us out here to freeze to death.'

Scaurus stood abruptly. 'Don't you talk like that about the Empire.'

Drustan was instantly on his feet. 'I'll say what I like about those fuckers in Rome who chew up men like me and you.'

'Like you, maybe, you British barbarian cocksucker. Not me. My family goes back generations in Rome. My great-great grandfather was a senator.'

Drustan laughed scornfully. 'And your great-great grandmother was a slave, and so were her bastard children, and your family has lived in the Subura for generations.'

Scaurus was almost too quick to follow with the eye. He leapt forward, his hands reaching for Drustan's neck. Sparks and embers scattered into the dark air as he caught the fire with his trailing foot. He bowled Drustan over backwards, and before Drustan or anyone else could react, he was raining blows down onto the centre of his face. Drustan was no weakling, and when he got his hands between them, he was able to fend off some of the worst of the punches, but he was still struggling until Atius and Memnon grabbed Scaurus by the shoulders and hauled him off.

They had to restrain him for some time, struggling and spitting, until he was calm enough to be carefully let go.

Drustan wiped the blood from his moustache and beard, where it had spurted out of his nose.

'I should kill you for that, bastard,' said Drustan.

'Insult my family again, barbarian, and I'll slit your throat before you can draw breath.'

'Enough,' barked Atius, and the two belligerents sulkily simmered down.

'I should have you both caned,' said Atius. 'That sort of indiscipline has no place in the Roman army.' Atius was aware his own track record made this rather hypocritical, but he wasn't going to get into that now. 'Let me remind you that not only do we have a mission to fulfill, we are in enemy territory, and our lives are in danger both from hostile Germans and the weather. This sort of behaviour could cost us all our lives.'

Scaurus and Drustan looked shamefaced, then with some hesitation, Scaurus held out his hand. Grudgingly at first, Drustan took it, but Scaurus gripped it tight and shook it hard, pulling Drustan into a hug and clapping his back.

'I'm sorry, barbarian,' said Scaurus. 'I am a bit sensitive about Rome and my family.'

Drustan hesitated, then returned the hug.

'I'm sorry too, Roman. I shouldn't have teased you. Family and homeland are important.'

And just like that, like a summer storm that crashes overhead and is gone, it was over, and only the blood on Drustan's face and some scattered ashes showed that anything at all had transpired.

'It's time to hit the tents. Bed, everyone. That includes you, Eustachys. Memnon, go and relieve Toutorix. Scaurus, you're up after Memnon, then Aldric, then me until dawn.'

'Why doesn't Eustachys have to keep watch?' complained Scaurus, as he did every night.

'How many times do I have to say this? He is not a soldier. What use would he be if he came across an enemy?'

'He can scream, can't he? I bet he can scream real good.'

'Bed,' said Atius firmly, in the tone of voice he had heard Silus use on his dog Issa. Scaurus shuffled off to his tent like a reluctant child.

Atius held the flap of the tent open for Eustachys, and then followed him inside. It was cool, but the leather walls keeping the wind out helped with the temperature, and the layers of wool beneath Atius' tunic stopped him from freezing solid. He placed his pack as best he could to make a pillow, curled up into a tight ball, and closed his eyes.

'How are we ever going to make it with that rabble?'

Atius suppressed a sigh.

'They are hand-picked.'

'By whom? A blind idiot?'

'Look…' Atius began, but was interrupted by a shout.

'Centurion! Atius!' It was Memnon's deep booming voice.

Atius was out of the tent like a cat after a mouse. He grabbed a burning brand from the fire and followed the sound of Memnon's voice. The others were swiftly out of their tents too, drawing swords as they stumbled to their feet.

Atius reached Memnon, who was standing still, sword drawn, wide eyes darting around him.

At his feet lay Toutorix, on his back, staring blankly at the dark sky.

A thick spear, rimed with frozen blood, protruded from his chest.

Martius 213 AD

He didn't know who he would miss more, Tituria or Issa. The little dog loved him unconditionally, and was his only link to his past, his family and the country of his birth. With Tituria, their relationship was more nuanced. It couldn't be otherwise, given their history, the circumstances of their meeting. She could never forgive him for what he'd done to her family, while at the same time she would never stop being grateful for his other actions. And he was all she had now.

Issa didn't understand his departure. She tolerated his hug and his kiss on her forehead, then wriggled to get down. She ran around the atrium, sniffing for food, then bent down to drink from the impluvium. The fish that had been lazily circling near the surface splashed out of her way.

Tituria understood he had to go, but though she tried to be the embodiment of Roman womanly fortitude, she was still a child, and as he embraced her, the tears broke through into uncontrollable sobs. He stroked her hair, feeling guilty. Almost guilty enough to tell Oclatinius to go fuck himself.

But it was Atius that was in trouble. He couldn't abandon his friend, not even for the feelings of this little girl he loved almost as much as his own daughter. He squeezed her tight, then extricated himself. He put his hands on her shoulders and looked down at her.

'I *will* be back.'

She nodded, though he saw the disbelief in her tear-filled eyes.

'I promise,' he said. 'And maybe, if I do this service for the Emperor, I can persuade him to reconsider your exile.'

She looked up at him with a little hope. But then her expression became sad.

'And if he did? Where would I go? I have no home, no family.'

'You have me. We could go anywhere together. Rome. Britain. Alexandria.' Those were most of the places he had personally visited, so were the first to come to mind, though he wasn't sure he genuinely wanted to go back to the scenes of such horrific memories. But it seemed to give Tituria some comfort.

'Alexandria,' she said. 'I would like to go there. What you have told me about the place, it sounds magical.'

'Then we shall,' he said, with more confidence than he felt. He had to survive this mission, get Caracalla's pardon for Tituria, and get permission to return before he could fulfill that promise. But he had to leave her with something.

'I have to go. The ship leaves with the tide.'

He stepped back, walked towards the door.

'Silus.'

He turned back.

'Please come back to me.'

He nodded. 'I will.'

—

Lipari receded into the distance. Silus watched it get smaller from the rail at the stern of the liburnian. He felt frustrated, full of pent-up energy he couldn't use. He was leaving behind the closest thing he had to family, sailing to the rescue of his friend, and yet it would be days before he even reached the port to disembark, after which he would still have to travel many miles to begin his search.

So for now he was stuck on this ship, with nothing to do. He looked down and realised he was gripping the rail so tightly, his knuckles had gone white. He released his grip and looked down at his palms, indented with the wood.

'She is a tough child.'

Silus started at the voice coming from over his right shoulder. For all his own skills, he was always amazed by how Oclatinius could move around so silently.

'I know,' he said, turning his gaze back out to sea. 'But a child, all the same.'

Oclatinius stood next to him at the rail. Gulls circled in the wake, occasionally diving into the foam, sometimes emerging with a wriggling fish, sometimes empty-beaked and cawwing in frustration. They stood a while in silence. Then Oclatinius clapped him on the shoulder.

'Come and eat. We have much to discuss.'

Silus looked out at Lipari once more. It had been a long time since he could make out any detail on its shores, and now it was disappearing into the haze. He sighed, and followed Oclatinius.

The spymaster had found two bags of flour to use as seats, and when Silus settled into the surprisingly comfortable makeshift furniture, a slave brought over wine, bread and olives. Silus took a loaf and broke it. He chewed laboriously, having to take a sip of the wine to moisten it enough to swallow. The wine tasted like vinegar, and he screwed up his nose in distaste.

'You've been getting used to the good life, Silus, in your self-imposed luxury exile. You've forgotten what military rations taste like.'

Silus scowled at him but said nothing.

Oclatinius sighed and took a sip of the wine himself. He immediately spat it out.

'To be fair, this does taste like whore's piss.'

Silus decided not to enquire how Oclatinius knew that.

'Come on then,' said Silus. 'Tell me about Atius. And for that matter, what's been happening in Rome? We got little news on Lipari.'

'Rome and Atius are all bound together, I suppose. Where should I start?'

'We seem to have a lot of time,' said Silus, gesturing vaguely at the journey ahead.

Oclatinius nodded, and took another sip of the sour wine, this time swallowing it like it was some sort of self-inflicted punishment. Maybe it was.

'The Emperor has… not been himself. Since the death of his brother. His mother has been distant, understand-ably. He has taken to drinking. Chariot racing for the Blues. And… other things.'

Silus waited without questioning. He didn't really want to know about Caracalla's vices. Their Emperor was another person with whom Silus had a complicated relationship. Caracalla had elevated him from obscurity, interceded on his behalf, rewarded him handsomely. But he had also asked him to perform deeds that had taken their toll on Silus, and haunted his dreams. Not to mention his exile of Tituria, which while understandable, since her father had been involved in a plot against him, was hard for Silus to bear.

'It has been hard in Rome too. His purge of his enemies has continued. Some because they are genuine threats, and some just because he needs their money. Thousands have died.'

'Who has been wielding the axe for him then, in my absence?'

Oclatinius clearly noticed the resentful tone, but ignored it.

'Most of the victims are noble, and so are given the option to take their own lives. But for the others, there are no shortage of volunteers. Some do it for monetary gain, some through loyalty to the Emperor, some just in obedience to orders. The outcome is the same for the poor sod who loses his head. Or gets strangled quietly in their cell. Of course, if they need something more entertaining for the games, they end up thrown to the beasts, or forced to fight with a wooden sword against a fully armed gladiator, or... well, you know what they do.'

Silus looked sideways at Oclatinius. Was the ruthless spymaster getting soft in his old age? But as long as Silus had known him, he had never gloried in death and suffering. Just saw it as a necessary means to an end on occasion. He wondered if the sheer scale of the killings was getting to the old man.

'Anyway,' continued Oclatinius. 'Festus and I decided Caracalla needed something to distract him, so we planted in his mind the need for something grand to augment his auctoritas and dignitas, on the scale of his father's victories in Britannia. Something that would secure his reputation as a commander and Emperor. Fortunately, Germania Magna appears to be becoming something of a threat, so Festus and I made sure he saw reports of unrest across the border from the German provinces. Real reports, but their importance may be overemphasised.

'Caracalla took an interest, and has been for some time now planning a big campaign in Germania. He has raised new troops from Africa, and left Rome with a great army. He went to Germania Superior and oversaw the construction and repair of the border fortifications. Then he gathered troops from nearby provinces like Raetia and Pannonia to prepare for the campaign. Unfortunately, the neighbouring barbarians noticed, and Pannonia was attacked by Vandals and Carpi.'

'I heard about that,' said Silus. 'Atius wrote to me. He said that Caracalla rode a hundred miles a day to get to Pannonia in a week and defeat the invaders.'

'He did,' said Oclatinius. 'With just his bodyguard cavalry with him, he rallied the local defences and routed the barbarians. Whatever anyone thinks of Caracalla, it was a remarkable piece of generalship.'

'I've never doubted his ability in the field,' said Silus. 'Now tell me more about Atius. How did he get himself captured?'

Chapter Two

Atius ordered a rest stop at around noon. There had been a break in the weather, and the sun was out, albeit distant, low on the horizon and cool. They set their packs down and took out water flasks and hard biscuits. Nobody spoke, nor even caught each other's eyes.

They had scouted the area surrounding their camp the previous night, but had found no one. In the morning light, before they had set off for the day, Aldric had pointed out human tracks in the snow. They had clearly stopped a short distance from the camp, hidden at the edge of the clearing, and it would have taken a decent spear throw from that distance to where they had found Toutorix's body. Atius doubted it was some local villager who had just happened across them. The kill was too accurate, and too bold. What local villager would want to risk the wrath of a well-armed band of travellers who were just passing through, anyway?

But who the killer was, he couldn't surmise. They had left Raetia the previous week, and none of the men had been told where they were going. Only he and Eustachys had known. Aldric had been questioned about his knowledge of the general area they were headed to, but it was only after they had left Roman territory that he was informed of the precise destination.

So how could a skilled enemy have tracked them in this forest, in this weather? It must have just been bad luck. A German tribesman, a young warrior out to make a name. He was probably even now being congratulated by his elders, while the women of his tribe fawned over him, and offered him their bodies. Fucking barbarians.

They had buried Toutorix as best they could. The icy ground was impossible to break, so they had covered him in branches and leaf litter and let the snow finish the job. Atius had said a few words of Christian prayer. The others had stood respectfully as he spoke the words, but only, he suspected, because he was their leader. None of them were followers of the Christos. And he was sure he had seen Scaurus, ever the traditionalist, slip a coin into Toutorix's mouth for the journey across the Styx. What Toutorix himself believed, he didn't know. The Roman pantheon? The Gallic gods?

To be honest, he wasn't sure it mattered. He had been forced to confront his faith in Alexandria, and he still didn't know if it had been strengthened or shattered completely. When one such as Origen, who inspired so deeply, had turned out to be just a fallible man, where did that leave faith?

He had more or less decided to ignore the problem, and just carry on as before. A faithful follower of Christos, but without the rules and restrictions applying to him personally. But when he was presented with a sudden death, unexpected, the old doubts came back.

He tapped Aldric on the knee.

'How far have we come today?'

Aldric bit his lip and looked upwards. 'Five miles. About.'

Atius tutted. It was slow progress. The best part of a week since they set out from Colonia. He thought they were making around ten miles a day, heading mainly east and a little north, deep into the territory of the Chatti.

'How much further to our destination?'

Aldric looked up and to the right, thinking for a moment.

'At this pace, still six or seven days.'

Atius looked around him at the men, not exhausted, but clearly fatigued from the half day's march. He could up the pace, but it would not be sustainable. There would be injuries, from falls to foot sores, and their defensive abilities would be degraded. His mother had told him Aesop's fable of the tortoise and the hare when he was a child, and though he had rarely put its moral into action, now was a good time to apply it. Slow and steady wins the race.

'Finish up, lads. We're moving again soon.'

His announcement was greeted by muted grumbles, but none spoke out loud. For all their rough edges, these men, who Oclatinius and Atius had picked from the ranks of the frumentarii and speculatores, were disciplined, and he hadn't yet had cause to regret his decision. Which made it all the more surprising that Toutorix, an experienced speculator, had been taken unawares like that.

Atius swallowed the last chunk of hard biscuit, chased it down with some cold water, stoppered his flask, and got to his feet. Most of the others rose at the same, time, though Scaurus needed a kick to get moving. Aldric led the way once more, Atius close behind.

Soon after the small band of soldiers had moved on, two German warriors stopped at the site of their rest break. They were wrapped in long, thick sheepskin cloaks, and carried spears as tall as they were. One stopped, and examined the indents in the snow. He spoke to the other in a deep, guttural language. The other nodded, and gestured at the footprints in the snow. Together, they continued to follow the trail left by Atius and his men.

Martius 213 AD

Oclatinius sucked air in through his teeth, and considered the question.

'The truth is, Silus, I don't know.'

'I don't know' was a phrase that Silus couldn't recall ever hearing from Oclatinius before. He frowned, but waited for the old man to continue.

'It was only by chance that we found out the mission had run into trouble. A band of Chatti warriors had been raiding near the border of Germania Inferior, stealing cattle and burning villages, the usual thing. So a century was sent out on a punitive mission. Of course, most had fled, but a small group were found drunk in the remains of a burnt-out, pillaged settlement, and brought back to Colonia for questioning and enslavement.'

Silus couldn't imagine their questioning was pleasant, although the worst excesses of torture might have been foregone, purely to preserve the captives' financial value. German slaves were prized for their physical prowess, although if captured as adults they could be hard to tame.

'One of them was in possession of a Roman gladius. A new one, not some antique they had found on an old battlefield. That led to some more focused questioning, and the barbarian eventually told us all he knew.

'Which it turns out was precious little. Still, he knew that a party of Roman soldiers deep in Chatti territory had been ambushed, and that at least two had survived. He had seen them himself at a temporary encampment in Chatti territory. Trussed up like hogs, he said.'

Silus pursed his lips. 'How much territory do the Chatti occupy?'

'How long is a piece of rope? Their boundaries shift all the time, as they migrate, hunt, fight. They have some permanent settlements, but no permanent borders. Still, we know the Chatti occupy a substantial part of Germania Magna, beyond the frontier, bordering with the Alamanni to the south and the Cherusci to the north-east, along with some small tribes like the Tencteri, Usipetes and Bructeri.'

Silus nodded, but the names meant little to him. He was aware that the situation east of the Roman frontier in Germania was similar to the one he was used to on the northern frontier of Britannia – a hotchpotch of tribes, feuding with each other, occasionally uniting in confederations to fight the Roman enemy, before turning on themselves once more. He had never been interested in the detail, however. Germania had always seemed a very distant, dangerous, and ultimately irrelevant land to him. Now, suddenly, he was travelling there, and he felt completely uninformed and unprepared.

'So how am I supposed to find him in all that space, in enemy territory?'

'If it was easy, I would have sent some Praetorians. Why do you think I came all the way down to Lipari to fetch you personally?'

Silus felt a little glow of pride at this, even while he knew he was being manipulated. It was true though, he had proven his worth time and again. And there would be no one more motivated to find his best friend. Still, the task seemed almost impossible.

'So you don't know how they were caught. You just know that Atius and someone else in his party survived.'

'Well…' said Oclatinius, hands clasped, twiddling his thumbs.

'What?' said Silus, his voice low and ominous. 'Tell me.'

'Well, we know two of Atius' party were alive, at least at the time this German saw them. We just don't know which two.'

'What!' Silus exploded to his feet. 'You don't even know if Atius is alive?'

'Calm yourself, Silus.'

'Calm myself? You drag me away from Lipari, from Tituria, with some tale about Atius being captured, and now you can't even tell me if he lives?'

'You knew that would be the case. Even if I had accurate information that he was captured alive, it could be weeks out of date, and there would be no guarantees about his well-being.'

'But…'

'Besides, are you telling me that even if he was dead, you wouldn't do everything in your power to avenge your friend?'

26

'I...' Silus' shoulders slumped, and he sat down heavily. 'What was he doing in Germania anyway? He isn't a scout.'

'It's secret.'

Silus felt the anger rise within him again. 'Are you kidding me? Don't you think I need to know?'

'Actually,' said Oclatinius, and now his voice was iron and ice, 'no, you don't need to know. In fact, knowing too much is the real problem here.'

Silus balled his fists, clenched and unclenched his jaw. When he trusted himself to speak, he said, 'Tell me what you can.'

Oclatinius too seemed to need a moment to compose himself. Every so often, Silus got a glimpse of something, a little thing that made him realise the old man was not made of stone. But it was rare.

'He wasn't even supposed to be on the mission. The idiot speculator who was supposed to lead it broke his leg. We needed someone reliable and experienced, and you weren't available.'

Silus wondered if Oclatinius was trying to make him feel guilty, that he wasn't by Atius' side, that he hadn't been there to save him. There was no need. He was already beating himself up for that.

'Is there anything you can tell me about the mission?'

'A little. Atius and his men had to escort one of Festus' men, a Greek called Eustachys.'

'Festus?' asked Silus suspiciously.

'Festus is the Commander of the Sacred Bedchamber, and is closely involved with intelligence gathering. Mainly within the Empire's frontiers, it must be said. But this fell within his remit. His man Eustachys was to travel to meet a Chatti noble, to discuss various matters with him.'

'What sort of matters?'

'Confidential ones,' said Oclatinius firmly. 'But there lies part of the problem. If Eustachys is one of the captured men, he may reveal the detail of the Emperor's military plans.'

'You sent someone into enemy territory who had the Emperor's plans in his head?' Silus gasped in disbelief.

'Festus did, not I,' corrected Oclatinius. 'And he is profoundly sorry. But it was necessary, for reasons I can't discuss, that Festus' representative knew the Emperor's intentions.'

'And what has Caracalla made of this development?'

'The Emperor doesn't know.'

Silus raised his eyebrows. 'Don't you think he might be displeased to find out?'

'About as displeased to know that his top-secret plans may have fallen into the hands of the enemy.'

'But isn't it Festus' fault? Surely you can just blame him? Aren't you taking a risk by protecting that man?'

Oclatinius shrugged.

'It's not like you to take unnecessary risks,' said Silus. 'What has Festus got on you?'

Oclatinius' face turned instantly to thunder and he seemed to grow and swell, to loom over Silus like a giant storm cloud.

'You dare to suggest I am being held to blackmail? I, Oclatinius, leader of the Arcani? What do you think would happen to someone who attempted to blackmail me?'

Silus shrank back from the sudden storm.

'I'm sorry, sir, it's just – I was surprised.'

Oclatinius let the storm dissipate.

'Festus and I go back a very long way. Ask about it no more.'

Silus nodded and waited for Oclatinius to continue, but the old man had become introspective. When the silence lengthened, Silus prompted him. 'So Atius went into Germania Magna, with this Eustachys fellow and a small team of soldiers, on an unspecified diplomatic mission, and two of his team, which may or may not include Atius, have been captured, while the rest are… what? Dead?'

Oclatinius nodded. 'No one from the mission has returned to Roman territory, so yes, it must be presumed that the rest are dead.'

'And my task will be to find the survivors, rescue them, and escort them back to safety?'

Oclatinius hesitated. 'That would be the most desirable outcome, yes.'

Silus felt his guts clench.

'The most desirable outcome?'

'Don't be stupid, Silus. I have just explained to you the importance of the information Eustachys carries. If he has been captured, and it is not possible to rescue him, then he must be killed.'

A sour taste rose up into the back of Silus' throat. More killing.

'What if he has already told them what he knows?'

'There is nothing we can do about that. But Eustachys was picked for a reason. He is tough, and could hold out for some time. If his captors were truly ignorant of his mission, then they would have no reason to torture him for the information. But all men break eventually. The longer he is in captivity, assuming he has been taken, the greater the risk he will tell them everything. And we have to work on the assumption it is Eustachys in captivity, because the stakes are so high if that is the case.'

Silus nodded. Then a thought struck him.

'And Atius?'

Oclatinius looked shamefaced, but he kept his eyes on Silus. 'We have to consider the possibility that during the mission, Eustachys confided in Atius the secret intelligence. Therefore, if Atius has been captured, the same applies to him.'

'What?' Silus' voice came out in a roar, and it was his turn to show fury. 'You got me on this ship on the understanding that I would be rescuing, or at least avenging, Atius. Now you tell me I might have to kill him?'

Oclatinius took the anger like a boxer taking punches to the head and not retreating a step.

'As I said, it would be best if you rescued him.'

'But if I can't be his rescuer, I must be his executioner. Atius is my best friend. You only persuaded me to accept this mission because I thought I'd have the best chance of saving him. I refuse to kill him.'

Oclatinius sighed. 'Silus, don't make me be firm with you.'

'Firm?'

'You think you have nothing to lose, but in your heart you know that isn't true.'

Silus frowned, not following him.

Oclatinius looked sternwards, in the direction the boat had come from. Towards the island of Lipari. Silus turned to follow his gaze, and a coldness gripped his heart, made it suddenly hard to breathe.

'If you touch her...' Silus said, his voice little more than a whisper.

Oclatinius took a sip from his drink, regarding Silus steadily. Then he stood, and walked to the prow, where he held the rail and watched the waves.

Januarius 213 AD

'This mission had better be worth it,' said Atius to Eustachys. They were walking a short distance behind Aldric, who was making a good pace. They were out of the forest for the time being, walking across scrubby hills populated almost entirely by sheep who snuffled through the snow to get to the sparse grass beneath. They gave the odd farmstead they encountered a wide berth. They had no need to raid them for supplies, not yet at least, although Atius was worried if they had many more snowy forests to pass through, their rations would not last until they got back to friendly territory. Further, if they used the farmhouse or outbuildings for shelter, they would have to kill the inhabitants for fear of their raising the alarm about the armed band of foreign soldiers in their land. That didn't sit comfortably with Atius, not to mention it was a risk if any of the farmers escaped.

So they had sheltered for the previous night in their tents, in a small copse, and shivered through the dark hours. It hadn't been a popular decision. Scaurus had been particularly vocal, complaining that the lives of a few barbarians weren't worth them having to endure this cold. Atius had let him grumble. He knew which battles were worth fighting.

Being in the open was a double-edged sword. They could see a long distance, and none of them had noticed any signs of movement in the distance, any indication they were being followed. But equally, they could be seen from a long distance away. And it was not snowing now, so the tracks they left would be visible for much longer. He sighed. There was nothing he could do about it.

Eustachys had seemed to consider the statement for some time.

'What would make it worth it?'

Atius turned to look at him in surprise.

'What do you mean?'

'How can I answer your question, unless I know what you value?'

'Well...' Atius thought about it, then decided it was too deep, and flippancy was in order. 'I like beer. And women.'

Eustachys nodded, as if taking his answer seriously. 'In that case, this mission is worthless.'

Atius looked at his grave face for a moment, searching his eyes. Then he burst out laughing, and clapped him on the back. Eustachys' face too split in the smile he had been holding back. It was the first time Atius had seen Festus' man display a sense of humour, and it was the first time he had felt any real warmth towards him. Until now, this job had just felt like babysitting a particularly miserable child.

When Atius had finished laughing, Eustachys said, 'But in all seriousness. Do you love your Emperor? Do you love the Empire?'

Atius was instantly on his guard, his jovial mood evaporated in an instant.

'It's not a loyalty test, Atius. I may be a spy, but I'm not a delator. I have no interest in trapping or denouncing people.'

Atius relaxed, though not fully.

'Love is a strong word,' he said. It was a word he genuinely avoided, if he was honest with himself. Especially where women were concerned. 'I honour and respect them. And yes, they have my loyalty. I was born a free Roman citizen, and I am proud of that.'

'So what do you want for the Empire? Why do you fight for it?'

Atius frowned. He wondered if his answer would be different if he was in a tavern in Rome, rather than out here in foreign territory with his life in danger. Still, he tried to answer honestly.

'I want to increase the glory of the Empire. I want to keep its people safe.'

'Safe from what?'

'Threats from outside its borders. Barbarians.'

'Then yes.'

'Yes what?'

'Yes, this mission is worth it.'

Atius nodded.

'And can you tell me any more than that?'

Eustachys shook his head. 'There is no need for you to know.'

Atius didn't reply. He knew that Eustachys was right, but it irked him to be out of the loop. Still, he had a job to do, and he had been reassured it was important. Important enough to lose men for? To die for? He just had to hope it was.

'How much further?' yelled Scaurus from a few feet behind them, then belatedly added, 'sir.'

The sun, breaking through scattered cloud from time to time, was dipping in the sky, but had some way to go before it hit the horizon.

'We're making good time,' Atius yelled back. 'We will march for a few hours yet. The more ground we cover, the less time we spend in hostile country.'

'Isn't it time for a break then? Sir.'

Atius called to Aldric to join him.

'How many more miles can we cover before sun down?' he asked.

Aldric squinted at the terrain ahead. 'Maybe another six or eight?'

Atius looked back at the men. They were tired, but could go on.

'We march until dusk.'

He ignored the groans from behind him.

–

When Atius gave the order to halt to look for somewhere to make camp for the night, he was sure he heard Scaurus mutter something like, 'thank fuck for that'. He ignored it. If Scaurus had wanted to make a point, he would have spoken louder.

Drustan pointed to a wooden structure half a mile away, in a small valley beside a stream. It looked like a barn or byre, but the roof had collapsed. There was no sign of habitation in the vicinity, and there were no recent human tracks in the snow. Atius looked around him. There was no other decent cover nearby, from the elements or from spying eyes, so he nodded.

'We will shelter in that barn.'

They approached it cautiously. Scaurus crept up to the door. Atius was at his shoulder, sword drawn. At Atius' signal, Scaurus kicked the door in, and stood aside as Atius charged through.

The broken roof let in enough early evening light for Atius to see the barn was not in current use, but he still had to squint into the shadows and wait for his eyes to adjust before he was sure it was completely unoccupied.

He beckoned Scaurus in, and with the tough soldier at his back, he investigated every possible hiding place – behind a broken gate that was leant against the wall, behind a low wooden partition, thrusting his gladius into a pile of mouldering hay to make sure no threat lay within.

Snow had drifted into some corners, but the mud floor was dry in other places. There was an odour of old cow dung and musty rat droppings, but the walls, though draughty, kept the worst of the wind out. He called the others in, and they set about pitching tents in the drier parts of the barn, clearing away the debris of its previous occupants, human and animal, to make room.

'Shall I make a fire, sir?' asked Drustan.

'In this luxurious accommodation?' asked Atius in mock incredulity. 'You will be asking for underfloor heating next. No, we don't need a fire for warmth, so we will eat cold food and hard biscuit tonight.'

Scaurus muttered a curse, and Atius whirled on him.

'Or would you send a signal to every angry German warrior nearby that we are here, and end up with a spear through you like Toutorix?'

Scaurus had the sense to look abashed, and he set to putting up his tent without further comment. The others pitched their own leather tents, by necessity packed closer together than was regulation, though Atius was never a stickler for rules. Atius kept watch at the door until they were done, then summoned the men round him.

'Listen, I know this is tough. We lost a man, and we don't know who did it or why. The conditions are shit. And none of us know why we are here. Apart from Eustachys of course.

'But we are doing a job, for Rome, for the Emperor, for the Empire. A job we are paid to do. Eustachys has assured me this mission is of great importance for the safety of Rome against the barbarian threats.'

'Typical Roman army,' said Scaurus. 'Treating us like mushrooms.'

'What do you mean?' asked Drustan, and Atius groaned, knowing where this was going.

'Keep us in the dark and throw shit at us, don't they?'

'That's enough, Scaurus,' said Atius. 'We don't need your crap. Now let's all concentrate on getting the mission done, swiftly and safely. We have lost one man, and I will have to write to his mother to break the news. I don't want to lose any more. Let's look after each other, and let's stop complaining. It isn't helping. When we get back to Colonia you can complain till your arse falls off, but not before. Do you understand me?'

Scaurus nodded sourly, pinching his lips closed with his fingers.

'We will keep watch in pairs tonight. It means we all get less sleep, but it also means we are more likely to wake up again. Aldric and I will take the first watch. Does anyone have any questions?'

They all shook their heads or stared at the ground sullenly.

'Aldric, with me.'

The guide got stiffly to his feet, and followed Atius out of the door. Atius loosened his sword in its sheath to make sure he could draw it swiftly if needed, then began a patrol. Night had fallen, and Atius had to pick his way across the rough ground carefully. A seemingly level covering of snow could conceal an ankle-breaking rabbit hole.

Aldric walked beside him, similarly picking his steps with care. Atius halted them frequently to stop, look around, listen. Their path traced a small circle around the crumbling barn, then a larger one, ever increasing in circumference. Aldric said nothing as they walked, sullen and taciturn as usual. Atius quickly became bored and determined to draw Aldric out of himself.

'Remind me, which is your tribe?'

Aldric gave him a measured look, as if trying to decide whether it was worth his while to reply. Then he let out a sigh.

'The Brukterer. You call them the Bructeri.'

Atius had been told that when Aldric had been assigned them as a guide, but he had had too many other things to think about at the time, preparing for the mission, to give it more consideration.

'Tell me about your tribe.'

Aldric said nothing for long enough that Atius thought he wasn't going to get an answer. When Atius had almost given up, Aldric spoke.

'You Romans think we Germanic people are all the same. But we are as different as Romans and Greeks and Egyptians. There are dozens of big tribes and countless small ones in the region you call Germania Magna.'

'What do you call it?'

'We call it home. We don't have borders, we don't have cities. We have settlements and farmsteads. We move when we need to. We stay if we want to. We fight each other. We make alliances with and against each other. Some of us are artists, some of us make music, some of us are warriors. But one thing we all have in common. We do not live under the Roman heel.'

Atius looked sidelong at him. 'You don't seem to have much love for the Empire.'

Aldric shut his mouth tight, and said nothing.

'Not every man in the provinces loves the Empire,' said Atius after a while. 'Even now that they are all citizens. But they still pay their taxes, join the legions and auxiliaries. You don't have to be a fanatic like Scaurus to serve.'

Still Aldric held his tongue.

'So why are you helping us? Guiding us through your territory in aid of Rome?'

'I swore an oath to my chief. And he made me swear one to Rome.'

Aldric stopped abruptly, hand up. Atius froze, gripping the hilt of his sword. Aldric listened intently, then said, 'Nothing. A deer.'

Atius considered himself a pretty good scout, maybe not in Silus' league, but no amateur. Yet he had heard nothing. Aldric must have tremendously sensitive hearing. The guide dropped his hand and they continued.

'Your chief?' prompted Atius.

'Colonia was built on Bructeri territory,' said Aldric. 'And the frontier of the Roman province runs through our land. Our chief wants peace with your Empire.'

'Why?' asked Atius. 'If your people have lost territory, why doesn't he fight to get it back?'

Aldric let out a short exhalation that might have been a humourless laugh.

'Because he fears death.'

Atius glanced at him.

'I knew a man once, a legionary, tough guy. A veteran. He was afraid of moths. And butterflies. Anything that flapped its wings. He could hold the line in a battle against a Caledonian charge and keep bowels shut and the inside of his legs dry. He would barely break a sweat as he stabbed and parried all day. Yet if a moth got trapped in the tent with him, he screamed so loud you would think he was being impaled in a druidic sacrifice.'

Aldric grunted, the merest acknowledgement that Atius was even speaking.

'That,' continued Atius, 'is a dumb fear. The fear of death? I think that's quite reasonable.'

'For a Roman, maybe,' said Aldric.

'For anyone with sense.'

'I do not fear death,' said Aldric firmly.

'That's what worries me,' said Atius.

They walked in uncomfortable silence for a while, Atius keeping half his mind on his guard duty, and half on the barbarian under his command. But silence was an unnatural state for the garrulous Atius.

'You hate your chief?'

'Of course not,' snapped Aldric back quickly. 'He is my leader, and he has my complete loyalty. Maybe I would wish he was otherwise. That he had more iron in his backbone, more fire in guts. But what is the point of wishing for that? It is like wishing for different parents.'

Atius nodded. He didn't like the idea of a discontented German in their ranks, when they were in enemy territory. He decided he had pressed enough and changed the subject.

'How many more days' travel now, would you say?'

'Maybe three or four. If the weather holds.'

'And will it?'

Aldric shrugged. 'Pray to your Christos it does.'

They patrolled for another hour, then Atius led them back to the barn. He woke Drustan up easily, but Scaurus was snoring loudly, so he reached over and shook his shoulder. The legionary's eyes shot open and he grabbed

Atius around the throat. Drustan and Aldric grabbed Scaurus' arms and prised them apart. They held him until he stopped his wild struggling.

Breathing heavily, he looked around him in confusion. When his eyes came back to Atius, who was clutching his throat with one hand and wearing a furious expression, his eyes widened.

'Sorry, sir,' he said.

Atius glared at him, then coughed and spat a wad of phlegm.

'Scaurus, get out of my sight. Drustan and Eustachys will be on next watch.'

'Eustachys?' complained Drustan, looking askance at the diplomat.

'Me?' exclaimed Eustachys, just as concerned.

'Yes,' said Atius. 'With the watch doubled and Toutorix gone, everyone has to pull their weight. Does anyone have a problem with that?'

Silence.

Atius rubbed his throat.

'Wake me before dawn. I'll take the last watch of the night.'

Chapter Three

Martius 213 AD

The port of Aquileia at the top of the Mare Adriaticum was a decent-sized city. Silus was aware that he had been spoiled recently by his extended stays in Rome and Alexandria, and his perception as to what a big city was had been skewed. But Oclatinius informed him that Aquileia was actually bigger than Londinium, the biggest city in Britannia.

He was in no mood for sightseeing. He had done enough of that in the two vast metropolises, and although both places bore bad memories, he knew that it would take something special to compete with the incredible sights in either city.

Aquileia was nothing special. As they walked from the docks, they passed through a market that had some quality goods. There was a preponderance of fine glassware, crafted by local Jewish artisans, as well as amber jewellery and goods and ornaments of bronze and copper. Silus stopped and studied a pretty necklace for a moment, one of many spread across a stall. The stallholder was on him in a trice.

'Very pretty, sir. Very fine artisanship. Made with my own hands. It would look wonderful around the neck of your best girl.'

The stallholder held it up around his neck and put on his best girlish smile, the effect of which was marred by a mouth of blackened stumps from which wafted a stench that reminded Silus of a gangrenous limb. He tried to shut out the sight and smell, and instead picture how the trinket would look around Tituria's neck. He was missing her already, a few short days after he'd left.

'No finer in Aquileia,' said the halitotic vendor. 'The best price for you, too, sir. Where are you from? Africa? Hispania?'

Silus realised he must have picked up something of a tan from his time in southern climes.

'Britannia,' he said.

'Britannia?' The stallholder attempted a whistle, which sprayed spittle. 'You are a very long way away from home. What brings you to our city? Are you passing through or here to stay?'

'None of your fucking business. How much is this thing?'

The stallholder looked taken aback, but recovered quickly. He pressed the necklace into Silus' hand. 'Five denarii, sir.'

'Fuck off.' Silus dropped the necklace onto the table and turned to leave.

'Wait, sir. This is fine work. No finer in Aquileia. Made with my own hands.'

Silus paused, waiting for more. The vendor's spiel was obviously limited, and he had nothing else to justify the valuation, so bowing to inevitability he dropped the price.

'Four denarii for you, fine sir.'

Silus waited.

'Sir, I must feed my family.'

The mention of family caused Silus' jaw to tighten. The vendor had no way of knowing of Silus' tragic personal history, but he wasn't helping his cause.

'Three denarii,' he said, ringing his hands.

'Two,' said Silus.

'Sir, the amber alone cost that.'

Silus kept his gaze steady as he drew two silver denarii out of his purse and laid them on the table.

The vendor sighed, and picked the coins up. Silus took the necklace and walked off.

'May the gods give you all you deserve,' shouted the vendor after him. Silus ignored the double-edged blessing.

'I don't think it suits you,' said Oclatinius.

'It's for Tituria,' replied Silus. Saying it out loud gave him pause. The hardened assassin, buying trinkets for a little girl. A small part of him wondered what he was becoming. The larger part of him told the smaller part to get fucked.

'I guessed. Not to be boringly practical, but you are going on a dangerous mission into enemy territory. Are you planning to take it with you there and back?'

Silus hadn't thought about it. It was an impulse purchase, coming from a place of loss deep inside him. He looked uncertainly at the necklace he was cradling like a newborn chick.

Oclatinius smiled and put his hand out.

'I'll keep it for you. Until you return safely.'

Silus passed it to him gratefully. 'You know, sir, I can never truly decide if you are a nice person or a complete bastard.'

'Can't I be both?'

They walked on, past various temples dedicated to a multitude of deities such as the Celtic sun god Belenos and the Jewish god Yahweh, past shops and workshops and foodsellers, until they reached the tavern that Oclatinius had decided they would stay in for the night. Oclatinius paid for the room and a meal, and they sat at a table to eat.

A slave boy served them bread, olives and smoked meats, and the tavern owner came over with a jug of wine and two cups.

'Will you try out local Pucinum wine, sirs? It is world famous. The favourite wine of the Empress Livia, you know.'

Oclatinius waved him to fill the glasses and Silus took a deep swig. It was light-coloured and sweet, with a slight sparkle that teased his tongue.

'Not bad,' he commented. He still felt a slight uneasiness in his stomach from the sea journey. Not full-on nausea, but his appetite was reduced, so he picked at the meats and dates unenthusiastically.

'Now we are back on dry land, what next?'

'Now we eat and sleep. Tomorrow, we ride for Colonia.'

Of course they would be riding. Sore arse and chafed thighs, how I've missed you, thought Silus.

'We can pick up horses from the cursus publicus along the way. We can be in Colonia in six days with regular horse changes, if we ride hard.'

Silus' buttocks clenched involuntarily. This was going to be painful.

Januarius 213 AD

Three or four days, if the weather held, Aldric had said. The weather did not hold. When Atius was roused for his second watch of the night, a blizzard had whipped up. The wind was whistling around the holes in the roof, bringing clouds of snowflakes through. Aldric and Atius went outside to patrol, but even with torches, visibility was close to nil. Atius pulled his cloak tight around him and over his mouth and nose, but the wind scourged them with a whip made of ice. They made a circuit around the barn, but Atius could see so little it was pointless, and they retreated to the barn. They stood watch within the door, only partially sheltered. Atius wished that he hadn't ordered Scaurus to kick it down.

The snow didn't let up, and by the time day broke, drifts had built up in the corners of the barn. He woke the sleeping soldiers, being careful to prod Scaurus awake with the tip of his foot, keeping a respectful distance. When they were all roused, Atius went outside. He got no more than a few feet from the door. The snow had drifted up to his waist in places, and it was still coming down heavily.

He went back inside and beckoned Aldric over.

'It's deep, and still snowing hard. Can we make any progress today?'

'Little,' said the German. 'It will be difficult marching, and I might not be able to find the way.'

'Fine,' said Atius. 'We wait it out.'

–

It kept snowing heavily all day. At intervals, Atius had the men shovelling snow into heaps in the corner of the barn, to prevent it forming drifts in the part they had camped in, though it was like bailing out a leaking boat. After some nagging and pleading from the men, Atius grudgingly allowed them to build a fire. No one would be able to see the smoke for more than a dozen feet, and even the most dedicated warrior would want to take shelter from this weather.

Though much of the smoke went through the hole in the roof, enough lingered inside to burn Atius' throat. But the warmth was welcome, and they all clustered round the flames, except for whoever's turn it was to keep watch by the door.

Drustan melted some snow in a pot and threw in some dried meat and some roots and mushrooms he had foraged along the way. Soon the bubbling stew was making everyone's mouths water. Scaurus tried to dip his cup into it, but Drustan slapped him away.

'Patience. It takes time for the flavour to come through.'

'Fuck the flavour. I'm so hungry I would eat a rotten dog if it was cooked.'

Eventually, after a few delicate trial sips, Drustan was satisfied, and doled out the broth. Atius blew on it, eager to eat but able to hold back long enough to avoid burning his tongue. That was a change, he reflected wryly. When had he started being able to delay his gratification?

Scaurus finished first, and so was able to use some bread to clean out Drustan's pot before anyone could protest. Drustan reached for the stew-soaked loaf but Scaurus shoved it whole into his mouth, chewed quickly, swallowed and then stuck his tongue out at Drustan, still covered in bits of bread and meat.

'You're disgusting, Scaurus,' said Memnon in a deep, disappointed voice.

Scaurus belched in reply and Memnon screwed up his face and turned his head aside.

'Why did you join the legions anyway, Memnon?' asked Scaurus.

Memnon cocked his head to one side.

'For the same reason as you, probably, Scaurus.'

'Ha, I doubt it,' said Scaurus. 'I can trace my family back generations and generations in the city of Rome. I joined up for the honour of my ancestors. What were your ancestors, goat herders?'

Atius watched carefully for a sign of reaction. They'd been cooped up in a small space for a prolonged period of time, and he knew men could start to fight like rats in those circumstances. The discipline of the legions should prevent it, but it depended too on the men. These were good men in many respects, but he didn't yet know how well they could be relied upon in a pinch.

Memnon did not rise to the bait, though. Calmly he replied, 'My father owned a hundred cows, and my mother was a maker of pots.'

'Farmers and artisans,' said Scaurus. 'The sort of people the city needs to keep proper Romans fed and cared for.'

'Proper Romans?' Memnon raised an eyebrow. 'You forget that we are all citizens now, since Caracalla's proclamation.'

'I bet that must have been galling,' said Scaurus. 'Joining up for twenty-five years to become a citizen at the end, then Caracalla gives it away for free to everyone.'

'I didn't join up to become a citizen,' said Memnon.

'I fucking did,' said Drustan. 'It was the only fucking reason. And here I am freezing my arse off on a dangerous mission in the middle of nowhere, when I could have been in Britannia, fucking the local girls, drinking the beer, and making an honest wage that didn't involve my friends getting spears stuck in them.'

Memnon looked at him until he was sure he had finished, then continued. 'I joined up to see the Empire. To see other countries and other peoples. And I was bored. My parents are good honourable people, but I did not want to become a farmer.'

'You joined the army for fun?' Scaurus whistled. 'You must enjoy pain.'

'What about you, Atius?' asked Memnon. 'Why did you join? You were an auxiliary, right?'

Atius thought for a moment. It really wasn't that long ago. He was not a grizzled old veteran, not in chronological time. And yet what he had been through over the last couple of years…

His thoughts drifted off, and he stared into the flames as images of executions, murders, assassinations, riots and battles flashed behind his unseeing eyes.

'Atius?' Eustachys put a hand on his shoulder and he jumped.

'Sorry,' said Atius. 'Joining up?' He brought himself back to the present with an effort. 'It seems a long time ago now, but I think it was the girls. My mother wouldn't let me spend any time with girls. So I joined the army to get away from home, and to get laid.'

They all laughed uproariously at that, and all the tension was broken. Scaurus took out some bread and passed it round, and they smiled and talked. Atius returned to staring into the flames.

–

The weather didn't break for the rest of the day, nor the next night. But the following morning, the clouds had gone and the sky was bright blue, the sun reflecting off the fresh snow cover with a brilliance that made them shade their eyes. The journey was even slower now, with this depth of snow, but they were all pleased to be on the move once again. More than once tempers had frayed in those close confines, and Atius had had to step in to prevent physical violence.

They made their way onwards through snow that varied from ankle to armpit depth. But the sun shone all day, and if Atius turned towards it and closed his eyes, he felt he could just imagine some faint heat upon his skin. They marched largely in silence, concentrating each on their own myriad miseries, their frozen toes and fingers, their fatigue as they struggled on, gasping air that chilled their lungs. As it reached higher into the sky, though, the sun began to do its work on the powder, and snowmelt dripped off trees and ran in small brooks.

Aldric led them along a narrow animal track, the grass worn away in a thin line punctuated by cloven hoofprints. Wild deer or domesticated animals? Atius speculated idly.

The answer came suddenly, as they rounded a rocky outcropping and came face to face with a dozen goats and a startled boy.

The goatherd could not have seen more than ten winters. He was pale, blonde-haired, smooth-skinned and terrified. For a moment, the legionaries and the boy, separated from each other by the small herd, stared at each other in shock. Then the boy turned and bolted like a hare flushed by hunting dogs.

Atius was at the front of the group, alongside Aldric. The German guide didn't react; he clearly thought it wasn't his problem. Atius cursed and set off in pursuit.

But first he had to make his way through twelve confused caprids. The goats' shoulders barely reached to his knees, but they milled this way and that, and he stumbled over them, leaning down to push them out of the way, and kicking the backsides of the slowest. It took him only moments to emerge out of the other side of the small herd, but it was enough for the young lad to gain a decent head start. Atius sprinted, arms pumping, his ankles twisting on the uneven ground, scattered with rocks and pocked by hoof indentations.

The boy was quick. He was long-legged and skinny, and in his own environment. But Atius was an adult in his prime, also tall and fast, though maybe a bit too bulky for a prolonged chase.

The fleeing youngster turned and saw Atius gaining on him. He took an abrupt right-angled turn, and began scrambling up the rocky slope of the hill that bordered the path. Atius climbed after him, using stony outcrops as footholds, grasping snow-laden branches to haul himself upwards. One shallowly rooted shrub came away in his hand, causing him to slip back down the slope half a dozen yards before he managed to dig his boots into the icy ground enough to break his fall.

He was panting heavily by the time the slope began to plateau out, and his quarry had increased the distance between them even further.

But now the ground was even and level, and in a straight foot race, the child would never beat the man. At least, not this child, and not this man.

When Atius finally caught up with him, he grabbed a trailing arm and pulled. The boy swung round involuntarily, but used his momentum to bring his free hand around in a close-fisted blow to Atius' head. Atius grunted, head rocking sideways, but he kept his grip. The boy tried to hit him again, but this time Atius caught his other hand, and held them both firm, squeezing painfully until the boy cried out. He wriggled in Atius' hold and tried to knee him between the legs, although he only managed to impact Atius' inner thigh.

'Enough!' Atius roared and lifted him into the air, then threw him on the ground. The boy landed heavily and lay still, momentarily winded. Atius gasped the air back into his own lungs, and rubbed his bruised leg and face. Then he knelt down and lifted the boy up by the collar of his tunic.

The boy spat unintelligible curses at Atius, so Atius smacked him around the side of the head, a blow that should have been hard enough to set the lad's ears ringing. It seemed to do the trick, and he was able to half lead, half drag the boy back down the slope to where his men waited at the bottom.

'A dangerous foe,' commented Eustachys, straight-faced.

'Looks like he nearly got the better of you, centurion,' said Scaurus, and Memnon and Drustan laughed with him.

'He's got some legs on him,' said Atius, still somewhat breathless from the chase.

'Maybe some more fitness marches would be in order, sir,' said Memnon, joining in the ribaldry.

Atius smiled, taking it all in good part. It did no harm for the men to mock their superiors from time to time, as long as they were obedient when it mattered.

'And now what?' asked Eustachys. And everyone fell silent as they looked at the boy. He stared up at them defiantly, but there were tears in his eyes, and some had rolled down his cheeks, leaving paler trails down the dirty skin.

Atius turned to Eustachys helplessly.

'Why did you chase him?' prompted Eustachys.

'To stop him revealing our presence,' said Atius, knowing exactly where this line of questioning was going.

'And how will you prevent that, now you have caught him? Will you take him with us?'

'Of course not.'

'You will let him go? Then why catch him in the first place?'

Atius turned back to the boy. He obviously didn't understand the Latin they were speaking, but knew they were discussing his fate. Atius thought about where he had been when he was that age, living in Hispania with his mother, helping on the farm and dreaming of running away to join the legions. And of all the things he had done since, all those experiences that make a life, good or bad. Could he really take all that away from this youngster?

Let the children come to me, do not hinder them, the Christos had said. Atius wasn't too good at keeping the commandments of the Lord and his son, but he had vowed to do his best.

Vow. Oath. Aldric had taken an oath to obey his chief, presumably on their barbarian gods.

'Aldric. Would a boy of this age feel the need to keep an oath sworn on his gods?'

'Of course,' said Aldric. 'We are taught from our earliest age to respect the gods and oaths taken in their name.'

'Good, then tell him this. Tell him if he swears to reveal to nobody that he has seen us, for at least, let's say, the whole cycle of the moon, that we will let him go. And if he does not so swear, that we will kill him, here and now.'

Aldric gave Atius a hard stare then nodded. He spoke to the boy in their harsh, guttural language. The boy still seemed defiant, argued with him. Aldric spoke back firmly, pointing at Atius and gesturing at the sword at his waist. Finally, the boy's chin drooped and he gave a small nod.

Aldric took his knife out, grasped the boy's hand and sliced the palm. The boy winced but did not cry out. Blood dripped onto the ground, and Aldric spoke words that the boy then repeated. After, the boy seemed beaten, defeated, head bowed and shoulders rounded, looking like he would burst into tears at any moment.

'Is it done?' asked Atius.

'It's done,' confirmed Aldric.

'Very well. Let him go.'

'Are you kidding?' Scaurus had watched it all play out with silent bemusement, but now the child was about to be released, he couldn't hold back.

'Watch your tone,' said Atius, no longer brooking insolence.

'If you let him go, he will tell his family, who will tell the local elders, who will summon a party to hunt us down.'

'It's a risk,' said Eustachys, not directly contradicting him, but clearly expressing his reservations.

Atius nodded. 'It's a risk. But I will not kill a child in cold blood.'

'Then I'll do it,' said Scaurus, drawing his sword and walking towards the boy, who shrank back.

Atius put himself between the rough soldier and the scared child. Atius did not put his hand on his hilt, just crossed his arms over his chest. Centurion and legionary stared into each other's eyes in a silent battle of wills.

Scaurus looked away first. He sheathed his sword and stepped back, spreading his hands apart.

'Fine, you're in charge. But it's all our heads you are risking here.'

'I understand that. But he made his vow. That will have to be enough.' He clapped the boy between the shoulders, and pointed off into the hills.

'Go,' said Atius. The boy did not need to wait for Aldric's translation. He took off like there were hounds nipping at his heels, and was soon gone from sight.

'I hope your decision doesn't endanger this mission,' said Eustachys with a sigh.

'If that boy doesn't keep his oath, the mission will be the least of our worries.'

—

That night, they camped in a coniferous copse, the canopy of which had prevented most of the snow from reaching the floor. Scaurus was still unhappy, but his grumbles were all under his breath, and Atius did not challenge him.

When they woke in the morning, and they hadn't been massacred, everyone's mood became lighter. They broke camp and set off, and on the march, Atius shared his water flask with Scaurus, who gave him a nod and a grudging word of thanks. Much of the melt had refrozen into treacherous ice but the sun thawed it anew, and their way became easier.

Though they had time on their side, it was not limitless, and Atius feared the consequences to whatever the mission was of arriving too late. Eustachys too seemed agitated by the delays. Moreover, Atius had no desire to spend more time in Germania Magna than was necessary. Though they had seen no sign of pursuit since the death of Toutorix, and the previous snowfall would surely have covered their tracks completely, Atius still felt uneasy, a crawling sensation down his spine, which he thought was not just due to drops of sweat under his layered clothing.

By the third day since the blizzard, the snow had turned to slush, which though it was unpleasant underfoot, cold and muddy, made for better time. When they camped for the night, in another deserted barn, Aldric announced that one good day's march should take them to their destination, and the men gave a rousing cheer to that.

–

Some miles back along their route, a German warrior, wrapped tightly against the cold, fingered a small piece of cloth that had been tied around a branch. He showed it to his companion, who nodded and raced back along the trail, to update the main party.

–

The attack came just before dawn. Atius was in a deep sleep, dreaming about being buried alive in a snowdrift. He woke, gasping for air, to the sound of shouts. He was instantly up, grabbing his sword and looking around wildly.

The barn they had spent the night in was in better repair than the previous one, with a fully weather-proof roof and walls of interwoven sticks. They had avoided repeating the mistake of kicking in the door, which remained intact. The commotion was coming from outside, so Atius ran to the door and yanked it open. An arrow hit the frame, sending splinters into his eye, making him stagger back, blinking. As he did so, Drustan and Scaurus, who had been on watch, came charging in.

Atius wiped his eye, which was streaming tears. 'What the fuck is going on?'

'Fucking Germans,' gasped Scaurus. 'Out of nowhere.'

'How many?'

'How the fuck should I know? It's still dark.'

'Then fucking guess!'

They heard shouts from outside, coming from different directions.

'At least ten,' said Drustan. 'Probably more.'

'Ten what? Warriors? Farmers? Fucking wet nurses?'

'Warriors,' said Drustan. 'No armour, just bows, axes and swords.'

'Romans!' came a loud, barbarian voice from outside. 'Come out!'

'Fuck you, you barbarian cocksuckers,' yelled Scaurus.

'Scaurus, shut up,' hissed Atius. 'The more they hear from us, the more they will be able to judge our numbers, and our positions.'

Scaurus mumbled an apology.

'Is it the same men who killed Toutorix?' asked Memnon.

Atius looked around to see if anyone else had the answer, then he shrugged. 'How could it be? Surely it would be impossible to track us with all this awful weather we have been through.'

'I bet it was that barbarian kid we let go. I told you we should have killed him. Atius, this is what you get from being too fucking soft!'

'Romans,' came the voice again. 'You are trespassing in our lands. Surrender now and we will make your deaths quick and honourable.'

'What a tempting offer,' muttered Eustachys. The civilian was clutching his sword like it was a child's bulla, offering some magical protection.

'Don't worry,' said Atius. 'It's not an option.' He looked around him, assessing the defensive capabilities of their shelter. It wasn't promising. There was no brickwork, so everything could yield to an axe swing. There was a door that was similarly flimsy. There was one window in each of the two walls which formed right angles to the wall with the door in, small openings about a foot square for ventilation. Atius crept up to one of the windows, and risked a look out.

Though his field of view was limited, he saw shadowy figures darting around. The sky was a dark blue in the east, the first indication of dawn, but it would be a good hour before the sun rose enough for them to count their enemies properly.

He saw a man suddenly stop, peer at him, raise a bow.

He ducked back and an arrow flew through the window and thudded into a straw bale just to one side of Scaurus' midriff.

Scaurus yelped, and darted to the cover of one of the walls. Atius gestured for everyone to do the same, so they were out of sight and out of the field of fire of archers.

'I will count to a hundred, Romans,' came the barbarian voice.

'There must be ten of them at least,' said Scaurus, 'for him to have that many fingers to count on.'

Aldric shot Scaurus a glare, but didn't retort.

'When I reach a hundred, we will attack. You will die, or you will be captured, and wish you had died. I am counting now.'

The barbarian was either counting in his head, or genuinely couldn't count, and was just estimating. Atius didn't know, but he wasn't prepared to leave the initiative to the barbarians. He looked around at his men, refreshing his mind on their strengths and arms. They were not armed like legionaries – this was an escort mission, not a legion marching to war. But they wore light armour, and each carried a short sword. Memnon and Drustan carried heavy pila, the sort that were as useful thrust as thrown, and did not bend on impact. Atius and Scaurus carried light composite bows made of horn and wood. Eustachys had just his sword, and Aldric bore just a knife, which would be useless in this sort of fight.

He beckoned Scaurus over to him, and they stood either side of the small window. Atius nocked an arrow and gestured to Scaurus to do the same. He waited until he estimated the barbarian would be halfway through his count, then nodded to Scaurus.

They aimed their bows through the window, scanned for targets, then loosed almost simultaneously. Atius' target moved at the last moment, so the arrow shot through the space his chosen warrior had just vacated.

Scaurus had more luck. His arrow found its mark, and his target went down. The ongoing cries and screams suggested it was not a clean kill, but that didn't matter. The warrior would be out of action for the rest of the battle.

They darted back into cover as soon as they had shot, even as three arrows chased after them. Two came through the window, and one hit the wall by the window frame, the head and half the shaft protruding through, half a foot from Atius' neck.

'So that is your answer!' the German roared. 'Then hear ours.'

There was the sound of whistling in the air, and some dull thuds and cracks as arrows landed on the roof and impacted the walls. At first Atius couldn't understand what they were trying to achieve, until one arrow penetrated the roof, half of the shaft protruding through, and he saw with shock that the head had been wrapped in an oily cloth and set alight.

'They're trying to burn us out,' cried Eustachys. Atius was already moving. He reached up and plucked the arrow out of the roof, then stamped on it to put out the flame.

But then he heard a crackling sound, and smoke began to seep in between the small gaps in the roof material.

Atius thought quickly. He wasn't facing an army, and they wouldn't have a limitless supply of fire arrows. Even if they had a plentiful supply of oil, which was unlikely for a small war party, they would have to start ripping up their own clothes for more rags, which in this weather would be reckless. He tossed his bow and quiver to Drustan, who fumbled, then held it.

He waited for Drustan to nock an arrow, then went to the door.

'Cover me,' he hissed, then flung the door open. He immediately heard the twang of a bowstring and ducked instinctively. The arrow, hastily shot, flew wide. Drustan and Scaurus leant out around the edge of the door frame and shot back. Their aim was similarly wayward, but it had the effect of keeping the Germans' heads down for a moment.

Atius leapt onto the low roof, distributing his weight so as not to collapse the thatch and sticks that were strewn across the beams. The first arrow he reached was smouldering in damp moss, and he pulled it out and tossed it aside. He crawled further up the roof, and reached two more arrows which had just begun to ignite the straw. He gripped the arrows mid-shaft and removed them, then beat at the sparks with his fists to extinguish them.

Shouts reached him from the Germans surrounding the barn. He heard more bowstrings, the hiss of arrows through the air. There were two more fire arrows lodged in the roof, and he crawled carefully towards them as missiles fell out of the sky around him. He tensed, waiting at any moment for a barbed head to strike between his shoulder blades. His skin tingled in anticipation as he worked his way over to the final two burning missiles. The first was easily disposed of. It hadn't caught any combustible material and so had all but burnt itself out by the time Atius reached it.

But the second had lodged into a beam, and the whole arrow shaft was burning. Worse, there was an expanding circle of fire in the thatch. Atius spat on his hands and grabbed the smouldering arrow. There was a hiss of evaporating spit, but he ignored it and pulled hard. It resisted, and Atius gripped tighter, gritting his teeth as pain shot up his arm. The arrow came free and he threw it over his shoulder, then smacked his hand against his sides to dissipate the heat.

That still left the fire in the thatch to put out, and he had no water. An arrow arced down from the sky and grazed the inside of his upper thigh. He yelped and his balls shrank up into his body. He did the only thing he could, and rolled across the flaming roof, using his body mass to starve the flame of air. He rolled onto his back, his cloak smouldering but doing its job, and the flames died down. He stared at the sky, at the bright stars and fingernail moon, and his eyes widened as he saw an arrow descending straight towards him.

Chapter Four

Martius 213 AD

They rode into Colonia just as the sun was setting. They deposited their horses with the office of the cursus publicus, and went to find a tavern for the night. Oclatinius knew his way around the Roman colony well, and Silus figured he shouldn't be surprised. In his time in the Arcani, he had likely travelled the length and breadth of the Empire.

Nor should he have been surprised when, as he sat with Oclatinius eating bread and lamb stew and drinking German beer, Festus appeared and drew up a chair.

Oclatinius didn't even look up, just finished his mouthful, then took a long drink from his cup of beer. Festus waited wordlessly, examining his fingernails, and picking some dirt out from underneath one.

Silus looked from one to the other, then shook his head, sat back and waited.

Eventually, Oclatinius looked up and nodded.

'Festus.'

'Oclatinius.'

'Silus.'

'Festus.'

That seemed to deal with the pleasantries. Festus turned his gaze on Silus, and regarded him appraisingly.

'You put a lot of faith in this one, don't you?'

'I would say he has never let me down,' said Oclatinius, 'but that wouldn't be strictly true. On the other hand, he is resourceful and skilled. And in this particular case, motivated. He is our best chance to get out of this mess.'

'Well, he has certainly caused me a headache or two.'

'You bring those on yourself, Festus. Frequently. You should keep a supply of willow bark on you at all times.'

Festus made a sour face. Silus regarded him steadily. He did not trust this man, and couldn't understand why Oclatinius had made no move against him. Palace politics was not his field, though, and he decided just to accept the situation, at least for now.

'So is now the time you tell me what I am really getting myself into? What was Atius' mission? How will I find him?'

Oclatinius gestured to Festus and raised his eyebrows. Festus reached over and pulled a chunk of bread from Silus' loaf, and chewed it slowly before speaking.

'The Emperor wishes for a great victory over the Germans. Although he led the army in Caledonia, and everyone who was there knows that the praise should be his, it is seen in Rome as his father's expedition and his father's victory. Germania will be his alone.'

Silus nodded and continued eating, moving his food out of Festus' reach. Festus frowned, and reached for Oclatinius' loaf. Oclatinius caught his wrist, and gently replaced it on the table.

'Maybe you would like to order your own?' suggested Oclatinius.

Festus let out a huff and flicked his fingers at a slave. 'Another bowl of this muck, and some bread, and a cup of your finest wine, for which I have few expectations.'

The slave bowed and hurried off.

'Well. The situation in Germania is similar to that in Caledonia, with the tribal rivalries. Taking on individual tribes is relatively straightforward. It's when they unite that they become a problem. And right now, they are showing some signs of unification. Have you heard of the Alamanni?'

Silus shrugged. He found it better to feign complete ignorance when having a topic explained to him. It gave the other person a sense of superiority, often false-placed, which he could use to his advantage at a later date. Though he could never smuggle that sort of ploy past Oclatinius.

'The Alamanni are a confederation of tribes, like your Caledonians and Maeatae.'

Not my Caledonians and Maeatae, thought Silus bitterly, but he supposed that to Festus, Britannia was just one big island.

'We aren't entirely sure where they came from. Some say they came from the Hermunderi, some that they are mainly descended from the Iuthungi, youths of various tribes like the Marcomanni who were crushed by Marcus Aurelius nearly fifty years ago. Regardless, they are the biggest threat in the area. But interestingly they are not the most hostile. They are actually quite romanised in some ways. Some of them live in Roman-style stone houses and use Roman tools. Some of their women even dress in Roman fashions.

'The Chatti, further east and north, are more of a threat. They are an older tribe, and took part in the massacre of Varus' legions.'

Silus shivered and made a sign of good luck subtly in his lap. Every man who served in the legions knew about the Varian disaster in the Teutoburg forest, and Germania was still thought of as a land of ill omen and doom, despite the successful wars against German tribes since that fateful day.

'Beyond them, further north again, are other tribes like the Chauci and Saxons. Were they all to unite, and someone could direct them, they could pour through our defences into Gaul, and unchecked into Rome. They are a much bigger danger to the Empire than the Caledonian tribesmen, who were only a threat to Britannia. If Britannia was ravaged, so what? If Rome was sacked, well...'

He let the words trail off, obviously believing his point was made. Silus personally would rather see Rome destroyed than his people back home, but it wasn't a choice he would have to make. He listened, outwardly polite, to gain what information he could that might be of use to his mission, but actually he felt like punching this smug spymaster on the nose. He sipped his beer and waited.

'Well. The point of all this is that Atius was conducting a man of mine, a fellow called Eustachys, on a diplomatic mission into Chatti territory. And in order for this mission to succeed, Eustachys had to be privy to some of the Emperor's strategic plans.'

Silus couldn't resist now. 'He went into enemy territory with Caracalla's military secrets in his head? Why didn't you just carve them into a big tablet and send them by courier to their chief?'

Festus' face darkened. 'You know nothing about politics and diplomacy and strategy. I judged it a risk worth taking, for the considerable rewards.'

'And with hindsight?'

Festus got to his feet, hands on the table, leaning forward so his face was up against Silus' own.

'Listen, lad. Oclatinius here might like you, but I don't. Continue to take that tone with me, and you will find yourself swigging hemlock in your next beer.'

'Sit down, Festus,' said Oclatinius calmly. 'I think we are all agreed that with hindsight, it was pretty stupid, whatever your justification at the time. But Silus is here to solve the little predicament you have put us in. We are all pulling in the same direction.'

Festus glared at Silus a little longer, then sat back down. The slave carrying his food and beer arrived at that moment, but Festus yelled at him. 'Take this muck away.' The slave retreated rapidly.

'Festus, do please continue,' said Oclatinius.

Festus took a breath and visibly calmed himself. 'All you really need to know is that Atius led a small expedition into Chatti territory to escort Eustachys on his mission. That expedition was ambushed, and two of their number were captured. Those captives may know secrets that it is vital do not fall into the hands of the Germans. You are to rescue those two men, or if that is not possible, kill them.'

Silus clenched his teeth. Oclatinius had already revealed this to him. He wasn't about to let on that he had no intention of killing his best friend. He lived with enough guilt already.

'Where do I find them?'

'That, we don't know.'

'Um. I have heard Germania Magna is quite a big place. Have I been misinformed?'

'You don't have to scour every pes quadratus. We know where their meeting was supposed to take place, so we can assume they were en route there, maybe even at the meeting point, when they were captured.'

'Fine, where was the meeting point?'

'Kalkriese.' Oclatinius and Festus exchanged sombre glances.

'Is that supposed to mean something to me?' asked Silus.

'It's in the Teutoburg forest,' said Oclatinius in a low voice.

'The Teutoburg... the place where...?'

'Yes.'

'Why the fuck did you choose to meet there?'

'It wasn't my choice,' said Festus defensively. 'The man they were meeting, a Chatti nobleman called Erhard, picked it. I suspect he thought it would intimidate Eustachys, give him an upper hand in the meeting. Maybe he even believed it had magic power, that it could influence the fates in his favour.'

'If ever a mission was ill-omened... Was this Eustachys left-handed, and did he break a mirror before he left?'

'Don't be sarcastic, Silus, it doesn't suit you.'

'Regardless,' said Silus. 'I don't know my way to this Kal... Kalkriese.'

'You will have a guide to show you the way. An Alamanni.'

'Fine. And a hand-picked squad of elite speculatores?'

'No,' said Oclatinius. 'Just the two of you.'

Silus' heart sank.

'You're sending me into the heart of Germania with just a guide? When Atius and a team of hardened soldiers were killed or captured to a man?'

'It's a different task,' said Oclatinius. 'You aren't escorting a civilian on a diplomatic mission. You need

67

to move quickly, unseen, get in and get out, with or without… whoever is still alive.'

Silus shook his head. 'Fine, fine. I just hope this guide you have allocated me is one tough bastard.'

Oclatinius and Festus exchanged a look.

—

Caracalla sighed and tugged on his beard. The evening banquet had been tedious from start to finish. The decurions, the local officials who ran the Colonia, had taken every opportunity to harangue him about their terrible lot in life. He had no sympathy. These were men from the masses of the humiliores, plebeians, without rank and social standing, who had been accepted into the nobility purely because they had the cash to be able to fund the public works that the city needed now. So it was galling to hear them complain about the cost, how building stadia and repairing roads and putting on games was already near bankrupting them, and now half the Roman army had come to their city it would be ruin.

He listened with half an ear to their pleadings, while his focus was on the woman on his right. Julia Domna at least appeared to be paying attention to the whining provincials, and made promises on his behalf which he had no intention of keeping. Still, it didn't hurt to keep them pacified. Passive rebellion by the likes of these men could lead to funds being withheld for any reason or excuse they could find, and this expedition was already putting a strain on the treasury.

His father had amassed a fortune in Rome's coffers, but Caracalla was doing a good job of working his way through it. It wasn't his fault. The bribes and donatives he had had to pay to keep the Praetorians and others loyal had been phenomenal. To be fair, his father's dying words to him and his brother had been to command them to live with each other in harmony, enrich the soldiers and damn the rest. He wondered if his father would be happy with two out of three.

As always when he thought of his brother, his mood soured even more. He took a big slurp from his wine goblet, and stood abruptly. The decurion, a stooped, skinny man with a bald pate rimmed with straggly white hair, who was discussing the pressure on the city's sewage system, stopped mid-sentence.

'I'm tired,' said Caracalla. 'I will retire now.'

The guests all hurried to stand and bow, but he had already turned away and was striding through the door. One of his bodyguards hurried after him, and he snapped an order for more wine to be brought to his bedchamber. The bodyguard dispatched a slave on the urgent mission, and Caracalla entered his bedchamber.

A slave girl was smoothing his blankets, and she yelped involuntarily when he threw the door open, then put her hand over her mouth in shame and fear.

'Get out,' he snapped. Then, as the girl rushed out, he yelled after her, 'And tell the Empress I wish to see her.'

He closed the door on his bodyguard, and sat on the edge of the bed. He leant forward and put his head in his hands, and he was still in that position when the door opened, and Domna's gentle voice reached him.

'You asked to see me, Augustus?'

Caracalla sighed. 'In here, I am not your Emperor.'

Domna cast her eyes down. 'You are always my Emperor, Augustus.'

'Come and sit with me.'

'As you command.'

Domna walked over, tall and elegant, and Caracalla let his eyes wander from her feet to her face, still shapely despite her increasing years. She sat beside him, her hands in her lap, looking straight ahead. Caracalla gritted his teeth, trying to suppress the anger. Just over a year since he had killed her son, his half-brother. And she knew it was self-defence. She was there. When was she going to get over it?

'Lie down,' he said.

'Yes, Augustus.'

Obediently, his stepmother kicked off her shoes and lay on her back on his soft bed. He lay beside her, stroked the hair out of her eyes, and kissed her cheeks, her nose, her lips. She made no response, just stared unblinking at the ceiling. He put a hand on her breast, squeezed gently, and she flinched a little. Then he reached a hand up the inside of her thigh, stroking, probing.

He smiled when his fingers came away wet. She might be showing no outward sign of interest, but her body said otherwise, he thought. They had shared love together so many times, before Geta's death, and it had been so wonderful. But she had been distant ever since. In public she was a proper and responsible Empress, diligent in carrying out her duties, an ever-solid advisor in councils. But in private, she was as cold as a dead turbot, and though never outright defiant, she made it clear that there was an unfordable river between them.

Yet now, was he finally making some progress against the flow? He willed himself to slow down, to be gentle. He heard her breathing deepen, saw her chest moving faster, could see the throb of a pulse in her neck. He felt himself hardening, and he pulled her dress up around her waist and rolled between her legs. He looked down at her, and for the first time in more than a year saw something other than reproach in her eyes. He held himself in his hand, fumbled for her, penetrated her. Her eyes flew open and she gasped.

Suddenly an image of his brother was superimposed on her. He had never before appreciated how alike they were. But the picture before him now was of that last moment of his brother's life. With Caracalla's sword penetrating his chest. His eyes wide open. Gasping, trying to speak, blood pouring from his mouth.

Caracalla's erection shrivelled like a punctured pig's bladder. Domna, who was gripping his back and moving against him, noticed the change and was still, looking into his face questioningly. Caracalla squeezed his eyes shut, tried to continue, but the image was still there behind his eyelids, his brother's bloodied, agonised face.

He let out a cry and rolled off her.

'Antoninus?' Even in his distress he noticed that she used his real name. 'Antoninus, what's wrong?'

He sat up, pulling a blanket from the bed to cover his shame.

'Get out,' he whispered.

Domna put a hand on his shoulder, the most loving touch he had received from her since... since that time. He took hold of it and thrust it away from him, stood, taking a step away from her.

'Get out!' he yelled pointing at the door. 'Get out!'

Domna jumped to her feet, hurriedly rearranging her stola, and swept out of the door, choking back a sob. As she disappeared from view, the bodyguard poked his head round.

'Augustus. Are you well?'

71

'You get out, too,' he roared, but as the bodyguard hastily retreated, he snapped out, 'Wait!'

The bodyguard reappeared. 'Augustus?' He was unsuccessfully attempting to disguise the tremor in his voice.

'That slave girl, the one who was making the bed when I came in. What was her name? Actually, it doesn't matter. Just send her to me.'

The bodyguard hurried off to do as he was bid, and Caracalla sat on the edge of the bed. The slave girl didn't look anything like Geta. Wouldn't carry grief and sadness in her eyes, the way Domna did.

The girl appeared at the door, her face pale, legs shaking delicately. He looked at her carefully, and saw fear, but no accusation. Then his eyes trailed over her body, her wide hips, her delicate bust, and he felt himself harden once more. He beckoned her to him.

Januarius 213 AD

There was a loud crack, and the beam beneath Atius split in two. It caved inwards and he fell through with a crash. The arrow followed him down, faster than his fall, but no longer aiming for the centre of his chest. Instead it hit the top of his collarbone and ricocheted off into the barn.

He landed heavily on his back, all the air leaving him in a whoosh. He tried to suck air to cry out at the shock and the pain in his shoulder, but couldn't seem to draw breath. Memnon and Eustachys were leaning over him, peering down. He breathed in hard, coughed, then breathed again, more easily. Memnon put out a hand and Atius took it to pull himself up into a sitting position. He prodded his ribs, wiggled his toes, then winced as he felt his clavicle.

Nothing seemed to be broken, though his fingers came away from his shoulder sticky and red.

With Memnon's help, he got to his feet.

'Did I get them all?' he said, voice strained.

'Most,' said Eustachys. 'There were two lodged in the walls. Memnon reached them by leaning out of the windows. They almost got him, but he is unhurt.'

Atius nodded and looked around. Scaurus and Drustan were watching him anxiously, while keeping half an eye on the windows for signs of attack.

'What are they doing?' Atius asked.

Drustan peered out for as long as he dared, then ducked back.

'All still at the moment.'

There was little sound now from outside the barn. The warrior wounded by Scaurus' arrow was silent, either belatedly discovering stoicism, taken away by his comrades or dead.

'Aldric,' said Atius. The German guide had his knife drawn, but had been keeping out of the way, in a corner of the barn. 'Who are these people? What's going on?'

'I don't know,' said Aldric gruffly.

'Well, what is their tribe? You can tell from their accent?'

'Just a few words, shouted in Latin. It's not much to go on.'

'Guess.'

'I would say Alamanni. You are in their territory, after all.'

'And their motivation? Just to kill trespassers?'

'Probably. It is their land.'

Atius looked across at Eustachys, who wore a sceptical expression.

'What does it matter?' asked Scaurus. 'Those barbarian bastards are trying to kill us. So we kill them.'

'I was just seeing if there was any way we could talk our way out of this,' said Atius, not concealing his irritation. 'We are trapped and outnumbered.'

'You can't negotiate with this sort,' said Scaurus. 'Barbarians. Foreigners.' He gave a meaningful look at Aldric, who bristled but didn't otherwise react.

Atius looked at Eustachys, and wished again that Silus was here. He was much better at taking command in these perilous situations, where clear thinking was required.

Eustachys said, 'He might be right, unfortunately. I don't know if they are definitely Alamanni, but there are certainly elements of that confederation whose enmity to Rome is unshakeable. They would have no desire to let us go.'

'So we have to fight our way out,' said Atius. 'We are in a tricky spot though, men. We are surrounded and outmanned, and we can't see them to shoot at. Thoughts?'

'We can't stay here,' said Scaurus. 'They will burn us out, or starve us out. No one knows where we are, and we have no hope of rescue. We need to break out.'

'We can't break out in the dark,' said Drustan. 'They will pick us off easily.'

'They are both right,' said Memnon. 'Let's wait until light and then make an escape.'

Atius looked around them doubtfully. There were no good options. In the barn, they had some protection, but it was illusory. It was no fortified legion marching camp, with palisade and ditch. It was a flimsy animal shelter that felt like it could be blown away by a strong breeze.

They all looked at Atius for answers, and he had none, but he knew enough about command to know when to bullshit.

'Very well. We keep watch until light. Then we break out. Eustachys, can we expect any aid when we reach our destination?'

'Maybe,' said Eustachys. 'I can't guarantee it.'

'Then we keep going,' said Atius. 'How fast can we get there, Aldric?'

'If we keep up a good pace, we can easily be there before nightfall. But if we have to fight every step of the way? I don't know.'

'Good. Listen, everyone. We are tough. We are experienced. We are fighters. We will not surrender to barbarians. We can get through this. But if we don't, we will die fighting. For Rome!'

'For Rome!' yelled Scaurus, thrusting his sword into the air.

'For Rome!' yelled the other legionaries, and Eustachys joined in enthusiastically, waving his sword around his head.

'Watch you don't poke your own eye out with that thing,' muttered Scaurus.

They took up watch positions near the windows and door once more. Atius moved his arm in a circle experimentally, pleased that the injury to his shoulder from the arrow was not restricting his movement to any important extent. Time passed and he watched for the sky in the east to become lighter, but the hue changed with frustrating slowness.

Just as he thought he saw the first signs of orange, Drustan called out.

'Sir, something's happening.'

Drustan was keeping watch to the west, where the sky was darker. Atius hurried over to him, keeping his head down.

'What is it?'

'Movement. There and there.'

Atius peered, and thought he saw some scurrying figures, flitting around like bats. He took his bow back from Drustan, nocked an arrow, pulled back the drawstring and sighted down the shaft. But the figures were too distant and too dark against the western sky for him to pick a target. He let the string go lax.

'What are they doing?' he muttered. They seemed to be running around with no real purpose. As if their sole purpose was to draw his attention.

Oh.

'Get ready for an attack!' he cried, just as an axe smashed through the northern wall, which contained neither door nor window. The axe disappeared, then came down again, splintering wood and making a hole through which dim light dribbled in. Atius saw a face peer in through the gap, wild-bearded, straggle-haired.

Memnon thrust his spear right into the middle of the face, and then pulled his weapon back. The barbarian fell backwards, his eyes rolled up into his head, his nose gone, just a deep bloody cavern in its place.

Two more axes smacked into the wall beside the first hole, attempting to enlarge it.

'Drustan, get over here,' yelled Atius.

The Briton rushed over, and he and Memnon stabbed with their spears to force the axemen back. An occasional cry came as a thrust found its mark, though it was impossible to tell whether blows were mortal, crippling or trivial.

'Atius, behind you.'

The cry came from Scaurus, and Atius whirled to see a barbarian halfway through the window that Drustan and he had been guarding moments ago. Before Atius could react, the German was through the window head first, rolling over his shoulder and regaining his feet. He had divested himself of any winter clothing he may have been wearing, and sported only a loincloth. Now he charged with a roar of anger at the nearest target.

Eustachys.

Atius was in motion at the same time as the German, head down, legs pressing against the floor to throw himself forward. But the German was nearer than Atius, and his axe was already descending.

For a civilian, Eustachys was quick on his feet, and handier with the sword than Atius would have believed. The German clearly expected no serious opposition from the unarmoured, rather slight man he had targeted. So when Eustachys neatly sidestepped the descending axe, and thrust his sword through his attacker's midriff, the German was taken completely off guard. The barbarian stared down at his new hole with amazement, and when Eustachys withdrew the sword, he clamped his hand over the spurt of blood.

Atius ran him through with his gladius, spitting him side to side through his chest, but it was completely redundant. The German was already dying.

An axe slammed into the wall again, and Memnon continued to stab his spear through once more, to repel the invaders.

The flimsy door suddenly flew inwards, rotten planks splintering and dropping off the hinges. A German, so huge he had to bend over almost double, came through, a second close behind.

Scaurus rushed to the defence, stabbing his short sword forward. The giant German batted it aside with his axe, then swung his weapon backhand, upwards. Scaurus ducked, forward and down, and the blade just missed the top of his head, but the shaft smacked into his temple and sent him flying sideways, stunned. The giant barbarian lifted his axe over his head two-handed, ready to bring it down on the prone Scaurus.

Atius lunged forward, and the tip of his sword went through the giant's larynx and out through the back of his neck, where it lodged in the door post behind him. Atius tried to tug it free, but the second German who had come in behind the giant was confronting him now. Atius turned towards him, weaponless. His new attacker smiled, showing surprisingly fine white teeth, and patted the sword in his hand. Then with the speed of an angry cat, he swung. Atius danced backwards, hitting the back of his head on a low beam, but just avoiding the tip of the blade.

The German was quick, following up the first swing with another, and Atius shimmied to one side, then danced back again, keeping his head lower this time, as the German stabbed forward. Atius looked around. Scaurus was still dazed, attempting to rise but only reaching his hands and knees. Memnon and Drustan continued to fend off the axes trying to chop the north wall down. Aldric was wedged in a corner, dagger held defensively in front of him, but making no effort to join the fight. And Eustachys was struggling with another German attempting to come through the window, brandishing his sword to keep the barbarian at bay.

For now, there were no more Germans trying to come in through the door, or the unguarded window, but Atius doubted that situation would last long. Their numbers were clearly not limitless, but they were much more numerous than Atius' party. He had to dispose of his opponent quickly. But he was at a disadvantage with no weapon.

He tried to manoeuvre himself round to where the giant was impaled against the door frame, but the German warrior was no idiot, and kept himself between Atius and his weapon. The German feinted, slashed, probed. Atius found himself backing away to the east wall. Something prodded into his back. An arrow shaft was sticking out, a previous volley that had missed the window and penetrated halfway through the wall. He reached behind him, eyes fixed on the tip of the blade before him, and tugged.

The German lunged at him, just as the arrow came loose in his hands. Atius jerked forward, twisting desperately as his momentum carried him towards the blade. Grasping the arrow shaft just behind the head, he stabbed it like a dagger into the side of the barbarian's neck. Bright red blood spurted from the entry wound, and the German grabbed at the arrow with both hands, his sword dropping to the floor. He attempted to withdraw the barbed shaft, trying to look at it from the corner of his eyes. Then he slumped to his knees and pitched onto his face.

Atius snatched up the German's sword from the floor and looked around. The attack seemed to be receding. No more barbarians came through the window or door. Memnon and Drustan had repelled the axemen, though the northern wall had huge rents in it. Eustachys had sliced open the belly of his opponent, who was on his knees, soggy, bloody ropes of guts cradled in his arms like a horrific baby. As Atius watched, Eustachys stepped forward and thrust his sword down beside the man's collarbone into his chest, the killing stroke of a gladiator. He yanked out his blood-soaked blade and wiped it on the barbarian's tunic.

For a moment there was only the sound of heavy breathing as Atius' men recovered from the exertion of battle. Then Scaurus struggled to his feet.

'Now I'm really fucking angry,' he said.

Martius 213 AD

'And how is...' Caracalla twisted his finger around in the air, eyes screwed up as he tried to recall her name. '...Tituria?'

'She is very well in health, Augustus,' said Silus. 'Though lonely in her exile.'

Silus stood before Caracalla's throne in his temporary headquarters in the Governor of Germania Inferior's residence. To his right sat Domna, slim, regal, solemn. Silus could feel a distance between them, in stark contrast to the closeness he knew they had previously enjoyed. Furthermore, Domna looked everywhere around the room but at him. He understood. Silus had been present at her son's death, some called it murder, at her stepson/lover's hands. He knew from his own personal loss how difficult it could be to be reminded of tragedy.

'Paying for the sins of her father, sadly,' said Caracalla.

'Yes, Augustus, quite rightly so,' said Silus. 'But I did wonder, with her father and his conspiracy gone, whether the time had come to reconsider...'

'There are always conspiracies,' Caracalla cut in. 'But that isn't why I ordered you here.'

The messenger from the palace staff had found Silus in his lodgings that morning, still sleeping off a couple of ales and some stodgy stew. He had given no reason for Caracalla's summons, and Silus had remained in suspense.

Oclatinius had met him at the gates of the governor's palace and talked to him in a low, urgent voice, out of the hearing of the Imperial bodyguards, Praetorians, and assorted spies and informants that always hung around the court.

'Remember, he knows nothing of the true nature of your mission. Festus told him that we had arrived in Colonia and that I was sending you into Germania Magna to complete some important reconnaissance work. He didn't want the Emperor finding out you were in the city through some other means, and raising his suspicions. But it is imperative he doesn't find out about Atius and Eustachys.'

'You're going to get me executed, lying to the Emperor.'

'Festus will kill you if you betray him,' Oclatinius had said. 'So make it convincing.'

'Why does he want to see me, anyway?'

'I have no idea. Maybe he just wants to greet an old friend.'

Now, Silus stood before the most powerful man in the world, and fought against an urge to flee, while his heart pounded in his chest.

'Remind me,' said Caracalla. 'What exactly is your mission among the barbarians?'

Shit. Time to improvise.

'I am to scout enemy troop numbers and locations, Augustus.'

'A man of your talents, for a simple reconnaissance mission?'

'I was told it was a particularly dangerous mission, Augustus.'

'Which tribes? Whereabouts?'

'The Chatti,' said Silus, dredging his memory of the conversation before he started drinking the previous night.

'And where exactly?'

Kal-something?

'I have a guide who will take me to the right area, Augustus.'

'Will you be gone long?'

'I hope not, Augustus, though I'm not sure the exact length of time I will be in barbarian lands.'

Caracalla nodded, his mild curiosity seemingly satisfied.

'I thank you for undertaking this hazardous mission for your Emperor and your Empire. Be careful. As soon as you return, I want you to report to me. I believe I may have a task for you, by then.'

'Yes, Augustus. May I ask what sort of task?'

Caracalla looked around him. Besides Domna and himself, there were only two bodyguards in the room, by the door. Nevertheless, Caracalla just gave a half smile and put a finger to his lips.

'There are always conspiracies, Silus. Fortuna be with you. You may leave.'

Januarius 213 AD

When the sun was fully risen, Atius ventured outside. The Germans had gone, taking their dead and injured with them. The only signs that there had been any disturbance were some patches of blood near the barn and a bit further out where their arrows had hit home.

Atius wasn't foolish enough to believe they were gone for good. They had wounded the barbarians' pride, as well as their bodies. He knew they would be back, and probably in greater force. This was their territory after all, where reinforcements could be easily found.

He probed himself cautiously for injuries. His collarbone was sore, the skin over it lacerated where the arrow had bounded off. His back too, where he had fallen through the roof. And his right arm screamed when he moved it, the desperate effort of fighting off his enemies leaving the sinews and muscles strained. He moved it in a tentative circle, trying to stretch away the tension.

Then he went back into the barn, where five anxious faces stared at him, waiting for news.

'They're gone. Get ready to move. We leave as soon as possible.'

The men didn't need to be told twice. In moments, beds were rolled up, packs were packed, scabbards strapped on. Atius cast an eye over the squad. Apart from a growing swelling on the side of Scaurus' head, they seemed to have come off lightly. He just had to hope they could get to their destination swiftly, without being caught in the open by the Germans.

'Let's go.'

He led the way out of the barn, his men behind him, and waited for Aldric to orient himself. The guide set off without a word, and after a moment's pause, Atius gave the command to move out, and he followed the Bruc-teri tribesman. There was a thin layer of ice over muddy puddles which cracked and crunched as they stepped on them, and if they were unlucky shot icy water up the inside of their legs. But at least they weren't wading through snowdrifts now.

Soon they left the scene of the skirmish behind and were once more deep in dark, menacing forest. Atius hated that he was so lost, so completely in the hands of their foreign guide. Eustachys at his side seemed to share his sense of unease, though no words passed between them, just unhappy glances. But Aldric gave him no cause for suspicion, and when he came to call a break in a small clearing, around noon, he felt they had made good progress, in what he thought was roughly the right direction.

They sat in a small circle, breaking out water flasks and hard biscuits and refreshing themselves efficiently. Aldric announced he was going to scout on ahead, and Atius nodded agreement. He watched the long-haired German pull his cloak tight about him and head roughly east. As he disappeared into the trees, Atius wondered again what motivated their scout. Blind loyalty to his chief just didn't seem enough. He thought too about the barbarian attack on the barn. Was it random? It was a large party to just be hunting, or patrolling this deep in their own territory. And if it wasn't random, how had they tracked them in all that snow?

He wished once again that Silus was there, that he could talk it through with his wily friend. But he wasn't. Atius was the one in charge. Frowning, he got stiffly to his feet.

'Are we off already?' asked Scaurus, not a little irritably.

'Not yet,' said Atius. 'Wait here.'

'Where are you going?'

'Just wait here, I said,' Atius snapped.

'Yes, sir!' Scaurus gave a sarcastic salute and went back to chewing on his biscuit.

Atius followed Aldric's tracks to the east. They weren't as clear as fresh tracks in snow would have been, but there were enough cracked puddles and muddy footprints to make it easy for Atius to follow. The trail continued east for a short way, then looped south. Atius wasn't sure why Aldric would need to head in that direction. He was supposed to be scouting their way ahead.

The path continued south just far enough to be out of sight and sound of the Roman soldiers' break spot, then headed back west. This wasn't right. Atius put his hand on the hilt of his sword and loosened it in the scabbard so he could draw it quickly if needed. He followed the tracks due west, moving swiftly but quietly. The trail now looped back north, until it intersected with their previous path.

And there Atius found Aldric, tying a piece of cloth around a low branch. It was dyed a bright red, standing out clearly against the greens and browns of the trees, the mulch and mud of the forest floor and the snow clinging to boughs and trunks. Beside it, an arrow indicating their direction of travel, had been carved into the trunk.

Atius approached quietly, to within six feet, with Aldric oblivious to his presence. Then he trod on an iced puddle, and just the slightest weight on it made it crack noisily.

Aldric whirled, and his eyes widened and his face paled as he saw Atius. His mouth worked as he searched for words, reasons, excuses.

'I was just... I thought I saw.'

'What is that on the tree?' asked Atius, voice even.

'I don't know, I just found it here. Something the locals put there to mark a boundary maybe?'

'I just watched you tie it there.'

Aldric took a step forward, extending an empty hand in a gesture of... friendship? Supplication? Atius looked at in suspicion, almost taken in by the distraction. Then Aldric's other hand whipped forward, pulling his knife from his belt and lunging at Atius.

His surprise assault might have borne fruit if it was aimed at someone without Atius' training and experience. An ordinary legionary or auxiliary, used only to marching long distances with a heavy pack, and occasionally standing in line beside his comrade, behind his shield, stabbing at anyone who approached. A man such as that might have the knife in his guts before he could respond.

But Atius was an Arcanus. He had seen the attack in Aldric's eyes before he had even moved. A tightening around the corners. A widening of the pupils. So he was already in motion as the knife flashed out, and the weapon harmlessly split the air where Atius had been just before he dodged sideways.

Aldric cursed, momentarily off balance. He recovered quickly, but it was enough time for Atius to draw his gladius and hold it out defensively.

Aldric could see he was outmatched. He was up against a real fighter, with a weapon with superior reach. His eyes darted from side to side. Was he looking for escape, or help? For a moment, Atius worried that the guide's barbarian friends were about to spring from behind the trees.

But no, Aldric was alone.

Yet despite the hopelessness of his position, the guide went on the attack.

He was no beginner. He ducked and weaved around Atius' sword play, darting in to lunge with his blade, forcing Atius to parry and leap backwards. For a brief moment, the fury and desperation of Aldric's attack dominated the fight, Atius on the defensive at every swipe and lunge.

But it couldn't last, and from the wild look in Aldric's eyes, Atius realised he knew it. He obviously wanted to die in battle, for glory, or to take his secrets to his grave.

Atius wasn't prepared to grant his wish.

At the next thrust, Atius twisted his body in a half turn to the right, letting the dagger glide harmlessly past. The attack brought Aldric close, and Atius thrust his elbow up into the German's face. Bone and gristle crunched, blood spurted, and Aldric cried out in surprise. He fell backwards, but Atius grabbed the extended arm with both hands, and brought it down against his knee, cracking it like you would snap a dry branch for the fire.

Aldric screamed, the knife falling from his hand, and dropped to his knees, cradling his shattered elbow. Atius watched for a moment, then stepped forward and kicked him full in the face, snapping his head up, so he toppled over, sprawling on his back. Atius dropped onto his chest, his knees either side, pinning Aldric down as he writhed and mewled. He grabbed the collar of his cloak and pulled him up, so his face was just a couple of inches away from Aldric's. The German stared back, defiance crowding out the pain.

'Toutorix,' Atius growled. 'Your fault, right?'

Aldric spat a blood-filled gob into Atius' face. Atius didn't so much as flinch. He just smacked Aldric across the face, and though his hand was open, the force snapped his head sideways.

'Let's try again,' said Atius, as he took another grip. His voice was low and harsh, a slight tremor giving away the effort he needed to keep himself under control. 'How long have you been helping your friends track us?'

'Go fuck yourself, you Roman cunnus.'

This time, Atius slammed him down into the earth, knocking the wind out of him. Then he stood, and began to kick the prostrate guide. Aldric curled up, trying to defend his broken arm, but Atius laid into his upper back and kidneys with his heavy boots, the punishment methodical and well-aimed, not in the least frenzied.

Atius paused for breath, then rolled Aldric onto his back once more.

'Last time. Who has been following us? For how long? Why are they trying to kill us?'

Aldric coughed, a paroxysm that sprayed droplets of blood over Atius' face and chest. Atius turned his face away to avoid the spray.

In that moment, Aldric reached out with his good hand, and grasped the knife from the ground where it had fallen. Atius had no time to curse his carelessness, just the briefest moment to react. As the knife arced around, he threw himself sideways, off Aldric, rolling across the muddy ground, coming to a crouch, ready to react.

But the blow was never intended for him. As Atius righted himself, he stared at the German, disbelieving.

Aldric had plunged the knife into the side of his own neck, all the way to the hilt, so the tip emerged from the other side in a gout of blood. Open-mouthed, Atius stared into the German's hate-filled eyes, and watched the awareness fade from them as a dark red puddle spread all around.

Atius slowly, painfully, stood upright and looked down at the erstwhile guide. Slowly, a realisation crept across him of how truly disastrous their situation was.

'Christos,' he whispered into the silent forest. 'We're fucked.'

Chapter Five

Martius 213 AD

'Are you all packed?' asked Oclatinius.

'I have a spare undershirt and a hat for the sun, I wiped my arse particularly clean with the sponge stick this morning, and I will eat lots of fresh vegetables and try not to fuck any women with rashes while I'm gone,' said Silus. 'Thanks for caring, mother.'

Oclatinius shook his head. They were standing by the city gates.

'So since I am about to leave, isn't it about time you introduced me to this guide?'

'Of course.' Oclatinius whistled and beckoned to someone behind Silus.

'I hope he can handle himself,' said Silus, turning to look. 'Oh, Pluto's arse.'

The young lad before him was taller than Silus, but probably half his weight. He had long, straggly, fair hair, acne and a feeble attempt at a beard which looked like the fluff on a piece of mouldy bread.

'Are you serious?'

'Silus, this is Odo. He is a warrior of the Alamanni confederation, specifically of the Lentienses.'

'I'm not a wet nurse, Oclatinius. I'm not taking a child with me.'

'Odo's tribe seeks an alliance with Rome against the Chatti. I can vouch for his loyalty, and he knows both Alamanni and Chatti territory. You will not find a better guide. Nor will you look for one, since it is my command that he accompany you.'

'But he looks like he can barely hold a sword.'

'He has proven himself in his tribe's warrior rituals. But honestly, if you have to fight your way out of Germania Magna, you're probably screwed whoever you take with you.'

Silus shook his head. 'And how are we supposed to communicate?'

'I suspect Latin would be easiest, since I doubt you speak any Germanic dialects,' said Odo.

Silus had the good grace to flush.

'You understood every word I said, and didn't react?'

'Insults only hurt if they are true,' said Odo.

Great, thought Silus. A philosopher too.

'You know where we are going?'

'Like the goose knows its way home in the winter, like the river knows its way to the sea...'

'Let's go,' said Silus. He hoisted his pack onto his shoulders, lifted a hand in the air to Oclatinius, and set off without a backward glance. Odo hurried after him.

Januarius 213 AD

Atius' mind was blank as he walked stiffly back to the temporary camp where the rest of his men waited for him. He was aware that he should be processing what he had discovered, calculating the impact of Aldric's betrayal, evaluating what it meant for the mission, and making plans to compensate for the change in their fortunes. But all he could think about was his fatigued and aching muscles from the two fights, so proximate in time, the sting from the arrow wound over his collarbone, and the hard, dull throb in his ribs and back where he had fallen through the roof. Beyond that, all he could summon was a deep sense of doom.

He did nothing to hide his feelings as he entered the clearing. His expression, his demeanour and the spatters of blood across his face were instantly noted by Eustachys, who leapt to his feet.

'Atius. What happened?'

The others stared at him in dismay, faces pale and drawn.

'What the fuck is going on?' growled Scaurus, rising slowly with his hand on his sword.

Atius slumped to the ground, gritting his teeth at the pain that even the slight impact caused as it jolted through his body.

'Atius,' said Eustachys again. 'Where is Aldric?'

Atius shook his head. He reached for his pack, pulled out his flask, and took a long swig, the cold water over-flowing and running down his chin.

Eustachys stood over him, not speaking, but waiting impatiently for an answer.

'Aldric's dead,' said Atius.

'The Germans got him,' said Scaurus. 'Cocksuckers! They even killed one of their own.'

'No,' said Eustachys, catching on quicker than the others. 'It wasn't them, was it, Atius?'

Atius shook his head.

'He died by his own hand. But if he hadn't, I would have killed him myself.'

Scaurus looked over to Memnon and Drustan, eyebrows raised, but the other legionaries simply returned confused shrugs.

'So,' said Eustachys. 'He betrayed us to his countrymen.'

'He did what?' Scaurus looked like he might blow apart with rage, like the obstructive rocks that Hannibal heated with fire and split with vinegar. 'I knew he wasn't to be trusted. Fucking barbarians. Traitors and cowards, every one of them.'

'Has he been responsible for all our misfortune?' asked Eustachys. 'Toutorix? The attack on the barn?'

Atius nodded. 'I caught him laying a trail for his friends to follow. He clearly never meant us to reach our destination.'

'Are we even going in the right direction?'

Atius thought about it. 'I believe so. My scouting skills are good enough that he knew he wouldn't be able to trick me by leading us astray. And he didn't need to, as long as the warriors following us could stop us.'

'Why did he do it?' asked Drustan. The Briton looked anguished, and for a moment, Atius wondered if Drustan felt any split loyalty to his Emperor and his conquered homeland. But Britannia had been Roman for nearly two centuries now, and Atius knew from his time there that except for among those in the northern and westernmost extremities of those isles, the status quo was accepted, and even preferred by most.

'Why did he break his oath to us?'

So that was it. Drustan was upset by the fact that Aldric was an oathbreaker.

'He explained nothing to me,' said Atius. 'He gave me no chance to interrogate him, either. But I believe he had

93

a higher loyalty, to his people, above the orders of his chief to work for Rome.'

'So, what now, *centurion*?' Scaurus gave Atius' rank a contemptuous inflection. 'What the fuck do we do now? We're lost, and we're being pursued by a superior force, in enemy territory, with no hope of reinforcement or rescue. Tell us, what are your orders?'

Atius looked to Eustachys, hoping to find inspiration, or at least support there. But Eustachys seemed as lost as the rest. Atius was the leader, and his men were scared and demoralised. It was down to him, alone.

'We go on.'

'We what?' asked Scaurus.

'The mission has not changed. It has not become less important, just because we find ourselves in hardship. We still have the ability to complete it.'

'We should go back,' said Scaurus. 'Find the quickest way back to Roman territory. We have no chance of completing the mission now. Even if we don't get massacred, we have no idea where we are going.'

'Maybe he is right,' said Eustachys uncertainly. 'Our chances of success without a guide are greatly diminished.'

Memnon and Drustan nodded and muttered agreement.

'Eustachys,' said Atius. 'This mission is vital, right? Is it worth our lives?'

Eustachys hesitated, looked around at the angry, anxious soldiers, then his shoulders slumped and he nodded. 'I believe it is.'

'Then our orders stand. We go on.'

They were one day's travel into Germania Magna, and Silus was already feeling the mission was hopeless. The countryside was beautiful and wild, and reminded him of Britannia in some ways. Forests, farmland, marshes, hills. The early spring weather was mild. A bit chilly, a bit wet, a bit muddy underfoot, but nothing he could really complain about.

But this place was just so big. How was he supposed to find Atius in all this wilderness? If indeed Atius was alive.

Odo, though, seemed optimistic. Despite Silus' rudeness to him at their initial meeting, Odo bore no grudges and chatted all day long with the garrulousness of an over-familiar barber.

'What made you join the Arcani? Have you ever been to a chariot race? Does it always rain in Britannia?'

Silus' curt and monosyllabic answers did nothing to curb the young man's enthusiasm, and eventually Silus ordered him to be silent unless he had something pertinent to the mission to impart. Odo grinned at the order, but kept his peace obediently.

They traced the route they believed Atius and his companions would most likely have taken to get to Kalkriese quickly and discreetly. The wild countryside was punctuated by frequent settlements, collections of stone houses that made a village, or farmsteads with barns, byres and a farmer's cottage. They bypassed these inhabited areas, but decided they would risk the open roads. Silus was dressed as a trader from a German tribe, with a simple hooded cloak, trousers and a backpack. He wore his sword conspicuously at his belt to deter bandits who thought they might be an easy target, but that was no different from any other traveller in these parts, and indeed many Germans owned Roman swords, bought, traded, stolen or looted from the dead.

At this time of year, the days were lengthening, although of course the number of hours of daylight remained constant, since an hour was simply one-twelfth of the time between sunrise and sunset. As the sky darkened that evening, Silus asked Odo where he intended for them to rest for the night.

'Don't worry,' said Odo. 'I have the perfect place in mind.' And then, sticking to his orders to be quiet, he shut his mouth and kept it shut.

The main road curved to the right, but a small track, imprinted with cloven hoofprints, led to the left, and Odo took them down this route. The track wended through open farmland, grazed by shaggy, long-haired cows and scruffy sheep.

A prickling sensation at the back of Silus' neck was his first indication that something was wrong. He cast Odo a sideways glance, but his young guide seemed as cheerful and unperturbed as ever. Silus surreptitiously loosened his sword in his scabbard.

'Odo,' he said. 'Where are you taking us?'

'Would you like me to speak, sir?'

'Yes, speak freely. Where are we going?'

'Somewhere safe, sir. You'll see.'

'How far?'

'Just round this hill.'

Silus looked around him. The countryside seemed too open for an ambush, but he still didn't like the fact that this young barbarian was leading him to an unknown place. After all, something had happened to Atius and his group. Might not the same happen to him?

They rounded the hill, and Silus saw, nestled in a small valley, a collection of stone outbuildings congregated around a central house that would not have been out of place in the more salubrious regions of Campania.

Silus stopped. 'What is this place?'

Two dogs that had been lying near the house on the track lifted their heads, and in a flash were racing towards them, barking furiously. Silus tensed, hand on the hilt of his gladius. Not only were the occupants of this farm now alerted to their presence, the dogs themselves looked vicious – huge, wire-haired brutes with lolling tongues dripping saliva.

Odo stepped forward and they leapt as one, hitting him full in the chest and bowling him over backwards. Silus drew his sword, ready to strike, to rescue his guide, if he could just work out where he should stab among the chaos of ball and flesh.

It took him a moment to realise the sounds coming from Odo which he had taken for distress were hearty chuckles, and the dogs, far from savaging him, were licking him profusely, as if he were smeared in honey.

'Ran, Modi, calm down,' laughed Odo, pushing them off him so he could regain his feet. He wiped his dog-spit-covered face on his sleeve, and fussed both dogs around the ears.

'Silus, meet Ran and Modi. They are brother and sister. Modi's name means courage, but it is his sister Ran here that is really in charge.'

'And what does her name mean?' asked Silus, sheathing his sword.

'Thief,' said Odo.

Silus grinned in spite of his anxiety of moments before. 'I have a dog who deserves that name.' Issa was a terror

97

for leaping into your lap at dinner time, grabbing a morsel from your plate and running into a corner with it, growling at anyone who came near until it was gone.

'So I ask again, Odo, though I have a feeling I already know the answer. What is this place?'

'This is home. Come on, Silus, meet my family.'

By the time they reached the end of the path, a small party had gathered to greet them. A broad, weathered man a little older than Silus stood with his arm around the shoulders of a girl a little older than Odo, willowy and tall but with a thin, fine-boned face, wearing a Roman-style stola and palla and a plain silver bracelet. Beside them was a boy, maybe a year or two younger than Odo, who was trying to keep his features composed. And just as they arrived, a plump, matronly woman dressed in a blue stola came bustling out of her house, patting her hair, which was styled in the waves and ringlets that Julia Domna had made fashionable throughout the Empire, into place.

The matronly woman rushed straight up to Odo and threw her arms around him, then stepped back with her hands on his shoulders.

'Look at you,' she said. 'You've grown again.'

'Mother,' chided Odo. 'I've only been gone a month.'

'And look at your beard,' she said, stroking his chin. 'You're becoming a real man, aren't you?'

'Mother, please. I have brought a guest.'

Odo's mother turned to Silus, looked him up and down once, then hugged him tight, crushing the air from his lungs.

'A fine Roman man, I see,' she said, 'in spite of this attempt to look like a barbarian.' She gestured at his clothing. Silus winced internally. So much for his subtle disguise – she had seen straight through him. He made a mental note to avoid close contact with other Germans on their journey, and he would just have to hope it was convincing from a distance.

'Come on then, Odie-boy. Introduce us.'

'Please don't call me that, Mother,' said Odo, and Silus couldn't help but be amused at the delicate shade of red highlighting his cheeks.

'I am Silus,' said Silus. 'I'm a trader from Britannia.'

'No you're not,' laughed Odo's mother.

'I am,' protested, Silus. 'Shall I show you my wares?' He had a few silver trinkets and copper cooking utensils in his backpack in case he needed proof of his cover story. But she took his hands in hers and turning them over, palm up. 'Look at those calluses on your sword hand. You fight for a living, whatever you are carrying in your pack.'

Damn this woman. She was perceptive. If Odo had half her astuteness, he could see why Oclatinius rated his skills.

'Besides,' she said. 'My son works with the Roman legions in Colonia. Why would he be in these parts escorting a trader? But don't you worry.' She patted his hand condescendingly. 'Your secrets are safe with me. Now, I am Ada, Odo's mother, as I'm sure you guessed. This is my husband Boda, my son Ewald and my daughter Ima.'

Boda, a big man no longer in his youth but still formidable-looking, stepped forward and gave Silus a bone-crushing handshake and a clap on the back.

'Can I see your sword?' asked Ewald in a squeaky, pubescent voice.

'I'm afraid not,' said Silus. 'It's not a toy.'

'I know that,' said Ewald. 'I use an axe in battle.'

Silus raised his eyebrows to Odo, who gave a subtle shake of the head.

'I see,' said Silus. 'Then you should stick to the axe. If you start to handle a sword, it will throw out your balance, and your aim with your axe will be off. That can be life and death in battle, as I'm sure you know.'

'Yes, you're right,' said Ewald. 'I'll stick to my axe.'

'Come inside, both of you. Boda caught a deer yesterday, and it has been roasting on the spit all afternoon.'

Silus caught a whiff of the cooking venison and his mouth filled suddenly with saliva, just as his stomach reminded him it was empty. He followed Ada inside, and was surprised to find himself in a small atrium complete with impluvium, in which a couple of fish swam lazy circles. A young boy with an iron anklet and a livid brand on his upper arm took Silus' cloak and backpack wordlessly.

Ada ushered him through into a room in which three couches had been placed in the shape of the Greek letter pi. The couches were generously strewn with plush cushions and the ceiling was supported with fluted columns. He was in the triclinium, he realised, yet this was unmistakably a German house, with a small altar of animal skulls in one corner, and frescoes representing, to Silus, unknown gods of sky and forest.

'Will you dine with us tonight, Silus?' asked Ada.

'Of course, it would be an honour.'

She showed Silus to the top couch, in the place of honour, and she reclined on his left, while Boda took the space to his right. Odo and Ewald took the next couch down on Boda's right, and Ima took the couch on Ada's left.

Ada called out something in a Germanic dialect that Silus didn't understand, and two young slave girls appeared bearing cups of wine and plates of bread, nuts and slices of steaming hot venison. Silus took a plate, and as soon as he saw Odo begin to eat, he tucked in voraciously. A day's walk definitely worked up an appetite, and it was good to fill your belly without dipping into your supplies. The venison was juicy and tender without being over or underdone, and it was flavoured with herbs that Silus couldn't identify.

'This meat is amazing,' said Silus to Ada. 'You have a cook?'

Ada shook her head. 'We have a small number of slaves to help around the house and the farm, but I oversee all the meals in this house myself. The recipe for cooking deer was taught to me by mother, and her mother taught it to her.'

'Your slaves, they are all German?' Silus found it hard to keep the note of surprise out of his voice.

'Of course,' said Boda. 'Where else do we get captives taken in battle?'

Silus glanced at Odo. Had he already discussed their mission with his family? But his face remained blank as Boda continued.

'Our people, the Alamanni, and the tribes that make up the confederation, have been at war with other German tribes since time began. The boy who took your cloak was from a tribe of the Saxons, taken with his mother while he was still suckling at the breast after some raid by the Chatti, and then traded to us. The girls are sisters from the Burgundi tribe in the east. We even have an Alamanni slave who helps in the fields. He was sold into slavery when he could no longer afford to pay his gambling debts.'

'You don't keep Roman slaves?'

'It is not, how would you put it… politic. We wish for closer relations with Rome, not to anger her.'

Silus nodded, and took a sip of the wine. He was no connoisseur, but it tasted good, sweet, a long aftertaste. 'I can't help but notice you are all quite… romanised.'

'It is common among our people,' said Boda. 'You Romans call everyone beyond your border barbarian. And yet here, we live in stone houses, drink wine, listen to music, appreciate art.'

'And speak Latin.'

'Quite. Of course we can communicate in Germanic languages, but we find Latin to be a better way to discuss the finer things in life.'

Silus looked around the welcoming family, and finally felt himself relaxing, that knot in his stomach that had been there almost without him realising since Odo took the track off the main road loosening and unravelling.

'So your people seek an alliance with Rome?'

'You didn't know this?' Now it was Boda's turn to look surprised. 'I was told our emissaries have made many representations to Rome about closer ties.'

'Well, I'm not a politician, I'm just a simple…' he nearly said soldier, but didn't wish to confirm Ada's intuitive guess, so he just said, '…a simple Roman.'

'Enough man talk,' said Ada. 'Tell me, Silus. Have you been to Rome?'

'I was last there just over a year ago.'

'Oh!' Ada exclaimed, clasping her hands together on her chest. 'Is it as beautiful as they say?'

Silus could think of many ways to describe Rome, and beautiful was not the first that sprung to mind. Violent. Dangerous. Dirty. But he knew that his impressions were coloured by his experiences there, and that Rome did indeed have places of genuine wonder – the temples and palaces, the columns and triumphal arches.

'It has some beauty, yes,' he said.

'And the fashion? Would I be considered fashionable if I was walking on the Esquiline hill?'

Silus took in her dress, her hairstyle, the gold and emerald necklace, the whitened cheeks and the kohl around her eyes. She reminded him of one of the older prostitutes in the Subura who made themselves up like Roman matrons to compensate for their fading looks.

'Absolutely,' he said. 'You would be the envy of many a Roman lady.'

Ada smiled in delight, and beckoned one of the slave girls to top up Silus' wine. When she had done so, Ada told them to begin the entertainment.

The two sisters danced, and one sang while the other played a reeded instrument. Elements of Roman, Celtic and Germanic music and rhythm were intertwined, producing an experience that was enchanting and a little unsettling. He glanced across at Odo, who was talking to his brother and laughing. He seemed to be paying little attention to the slave girls, which was odd since they were beautiful in a rough, barbarian way, and Odo was a young man, with all the desires and urges that engendered. Maybe he had seen so much of the girls around the house as he grew up that he did not view them in a sexual way.

Silus had no such inhibition, and admired the display. He had a sneaking suspicion that if Ada was as good a host as he thought she was, one of the girls would be sent to his room that night. Or maybe both. And after so long on Lipari without romantic female company, he doubted he would reject them. A year or so ago, he would not have been able to allow a woman into his bed, still wracked by grief and guilt about the death of his wife. Now, as he watched the girls gyrate their hips, he thought he would cope.

After the entertainment had ended and the dinner plates were cleared away, Odo's family quizzed him about all things Roman. Ewald wanted to know about Roman tactics in battle. Silus kept his replies vague, aware that, friendly as the Alamanni seemed, they were still outside the Empire's borders, and who knew when alliances and friendships could change.

Ima on the other hand wanted to know about Roman culture. What were the poets writing about? What plays were being performed in the theatres of Marcellus and Pompey? Silus was happy to tell her everything he knew on this subject, which was next to nothing. He was obliged to embellish a bit, putting together what he could recall from his time in Rome, with half-remembered details about Alexandria and a sprinkling of Londinium. His bluff seemed sufficiently believable for Ima, who hung on his every word with wide, strigiform eyes.

As the night wore on, he became aware that he was a little drunk, very tired, and had to continue a long journey at first light the next morning. To the disappointment of his hosts, he announced that he had to retire, so Ada reluctantly showed him to his room.

The room was lit by a single flickering oil lamp, burning what had to be imported olive oil. The walls were decorated with pastoral frescoes, and there was a marble statue in one corner that seemed to be of a Greek-style wood nymph. His bed had a goose feather mattress that was as soft as anything he had ever slept on, and he undressed, extinguished the lamp and huddled under the blankets, feeling sleep claim him almost instantly.

The squeak of the door opening was not much louder than a mouse would make, but in the dead of night, it was enough for Silus to be instantly awake. But he had sufficient self-control not to leap out of bed, screaming and flailing around for his sword.

Which was just as well, since, as he had suspected would happen, it was a young girl who stood silhouetted in the doorway, dressed in a simple white gown. He couldn't tell which of the slave girl sisters it was, and felt unreasonably disappointed that she was in fact alone. But he simply waited for her to come to him.

He heard more than saw her shed her gown in the darkness, and then felt her slide under the blankets with him. Her body was warm and smooth, but her kiss was surprisingly hesitant. He wondered briefly whether it was in fact unusual for Ada to offer her slave girls to guests, and he was getting special treatment. They were clearly Romanophiles. But these thoughts evaporated as she reached down between his legs and took a hold of him.

Soon, she moved on top of him, guiding him into her. The covers fell away and a shaft of moonlight through a high window illuminated her torso and her face.

And with a shock he realised his bed companion was neither of the slave girls, but was in fact Ima. Odo's sister.

Oh fuck.

But it was of course way too late to stop.

Afterwards, she snuggled up to him, her head on his chest, and he stroked her hair, staring into space. Wondering how quickly he could ask her to leave, hoping to all the gods that no one came in and found them.

Wondering how Odo would react if he found out that Silus had slept with his sister. Wondering if he had fucked up the mission almost before it had begun.

Ima was snoring lightly, almost a purr, like a contented cat. He shook her shoulder to waken her, and she stretched, kissed his cheek, and slid out of the bed. She collected her gown, threw it on, and disappeared out of the door, looking over her shoulder and smiling as she went.

Silus lay on his back in the bed, eyes wide open, sleep a very long way away.

Januarius 213 AD

Atius' scouting skills were formidable. What's more, the men selected for the mission knew how to survive in the field, each one more than able to get by on their abilities to forage and hunt, to sneak and to navigate. The only problem was the unfamiliar territory. Few civilised men had ventured this far into Germania, and what little information Atius had was gleaned from rough Roman traders and barbarian mercenaries and slaves. Eustachys of course knew their destination, but had little navigational ability to get them there.

So they marched through forest and hill and marsh, along muddy, slushy trails of half-melted ice, hoping that the end of their journey was as near as Aldric had promised, and that he hadn't been leading them subtly off course.

Atius was in the lead, acting as both lookout and guide, with Eustachys by his side. He looked back at the remains of his squad, straggled along the path behind, discipline and morale shattered. Toutorix and Aldric both dead now. Drustan, Memnon and Scaurus the only trained fighters left apart from himself. It was scant few to face down any enemy attacks.

'Maybe I should go on alone,' Atius said to Eustachys, out of earshot of the others.

Eustachys looked at him in surprise, almost stumbling as he took his eyes off the track.

'Why would you do that?'

'Because I'm the fastest, and the best at this. I mean, these boys are good, but they aren't Arcani. I could move quicker without them.'

'How would that help? You would still have me slowing you down. The least of them is faster than me.'

'I said alone.'

Eustachys was silent for a moment.

'You don't know anything about my mission.'

'You could remedy that now.'

'There are secrets I have been entrusted with that it is vital do not fall into enemy hands.'

'You think I would betray the Empire? You know what I have done for Rome and for Caracalla.'

'I don't think you would give anything up voluntarily.'

'Oh, so you think you would withstand torture better than me, is that it? I've been imprisoned, beaten, stabbed. I've got more scars on this body than you can count. What makes you think you could keep your secrets when a German witch takes her sickle to your balls?'

'Because I was taught by Festus.'

That sentence seemed to imply a great deal. Atius recalled what he knew about Festus, and realised that it was even less than he knew about Oclatinius. Powerful, ruthless, willing to play dangerous games. Inexplicably let off the hook by Oclatinius after the Emesene conspiracy, the plot to make young Avitus ruler of the eastern half of the empire.

A haunted look had clouded over Eustachys' face, and something in that expression told Atius not to probe further. He fell silent.

But Eustachys spoke.

'Maybe you're right.'

Atius waited, as Eustachys looked to be wrestling with a decision.

'The loss of our guide is a bad enough blow to our chances of success, but to know that the guide was betraying our location to the Germans means it is even less likely we will make it. Perhaps you have the best chance on your own, in terms of both speed and stealth.'

'I think I do.'

Eustachys nodded, his mind apparently made up. 'Very well, listen.'

Martius 213 AD

Silus had used the chamber pot, splashed water on his face, and was dressed and ready to leave before the sun had appeared over the horizon. He waited impatiently in the atrium for Odo, but it was Ada who appeared first, and insisted that he breakfast with the family.

'You will travel further and faster with food in your belly, believe me,' she said. 'Come.'

Reluctantly, Silus allowed himself to be led into a small family room, where the slave girls brought water, bread and olives. The rest of the family soon arrived, arranging themselves on benches around the room.

'It's been a privilege and a pleasure to have you in my house,' said Boda.

'You have been the perfect house guest,' said Ada.

Silus steadfastly kept his gaze averted from Ima, though he could see in his peripheral vision that the girl had her eyes fixed on him, the corners of her mouth upturned. Odo seemed oblivious to his sister's attention, but the ever perceptive Ada looked between Ima and Silus, and when she was sure no one was looking, gave Silus a wink.

Silus flushed, opened his mouth, closed it again and looked down.

'Now I know you can't tell me what you are doing or where you are going,' said Boda. 'But promise me you will look after my son.'

'I can look after myself, father,' said Odo.

'He thinks he can look after himself,' said Boda. 'And to some extent that is true. But he can be headstrong, and he lacks experience of life. Please take care of him, Silus.'

'I will,' said Silus, wondering if he would really be able to keep that promise.

He finished the small meal hastily, and rose.

'Odo, we have a lot of ground to cover. Let's be on our way and leave your family in peace.'

The whole household, slaves, dogs and all, came to wave them goodbye. Ada embraced both of them tearfully, entreating them to be careful. Boda shook Silus' hand warmly, clapping him on the shoulder. Ewald also offered his hand, and shook it as firmly as a boy of his years could. Ima merely looked up at him from lowered lids, her head tilted downward. He felt himself flushing again.

'Thank you so much for your hospitality. I hope we will meet again. Until then, I will do everything in my power to keep Odo safe.'

He turned, and marched back down the track, sure he wasn't imagining Ima's eyes burning into his back.

Chapter Six

Martius 213 AD

Two more days of travelling was enough to leave the semi-civilised parts of Germania Magna behind them. The change was barely perceptible hour by hour, but if he compared the settlements with those half a day back, Silus could see the difference. More wood, less stone. The inhabitants' clothing rougher, plainer. The further they travelled from the border with the Roman provinces of Germania Inferior and Superior, the less the influence of the Empire could be felt.

It was a situation that was to some extent familiar to Silus from growing up and fighting in northern Britannia, but the contrast was even more pronounced. The Germans who inhabited the area around the Rhenus had been in close contact with the Romans for more than two hundred and fifty years, since Caesar had conquered Gaul and Germania Superior. Britannia, separated by the sea from the Roman Empire and unconquered until a hundred years after Caesar's first expeditions there, had little Roman influence beyond the south-east of the island, and the people of the north of the province kept much more of their own identity than the people of the Roman German provinces.

Seeing how much Odo's family had wanted to appear Roman had impacted Silus deeply. His experience in Britannia and Caledonia had taught him that all barbarians hated Rome, and only ever allied with them for strategic purposes. Now he realised that some admired Rome, felt affection for it, saw its benefits, and wished to copy its methods, its customs and even its fashions.

It made his worldview more complicated than he had any desire for it to be. Romans good, barbarians bad. He was pretty sure that was how Atius viewed it, and there was a lot to be said for that degree of simplicity.

The thought of Atius made his guts clench, and he prayed to Mithras, Christos, Jupiter and any other god he could think of for his friend to be safe. Though he didn't really believe the gods would intercede. Either Atius was alive or he wasn't. And if he was alive, then it was down to Silus to save him, and no one else.

Silus had lifted his injunction regarding chatting as they travelled. Odo had shown generosity by offering Silus the hospitality of his family, and it was hard to be churlish in the face of that. What was more, he had slept with Odo's sister. As much as he tried to tell himself that it wasn't his fault, that he hadn't realised, he couldn't help the nagging guilty feeling that he had abused Odo's trust. Thank all the gods that Odo didn't know. That would have made the journey just too awkward.

So Silus forced himself to make small talk, mainly because long silences intensified his guilt.

'Why did you volunteer to help Rome?' he asked as they walked along a narrow raised track with sodden marshland either side. It was terrain like this that had meant they couldn't use horses, and much as Silus disliked riding, he would have put up with it to speed up the journey through this foreign territory. The further they got from the border, the less familiar and the more hostile it all felt.

'I hadn't really thought about it. I had just returned from a year with my mother's kinsfolk. They had taught me hunting, tracking, foraging, all the skills needed for survival. As well as how to use a sword and a bow, of course. And their priests had taught me Latin letters, numbers and logic.'

'Which tribe did your mother's kinsfolk belong to?'

'Alamanni, like my father. Her kin were descended from the Marcomanni, but they separated from the main part of that tribe after its defeat by your Emperor Marcus Aurelius. They have a reputation not only for cunning in battle, but also for an appreciation of culture, art and learning. Things the northern and eastern tribes have no time for.

'I had gone there intending to return as a fully trained warrior, ready to join the Alamanni warbands. My father on the other hand wanted me to stay at home and farm with him. But I had done a lot of thinking and learning while I was away. You see how my mother and sister love all things Roman, but they don't really understand it. They are like children dressing up in their parents' clothes for a game.

'I lived in my father's home, reading, practising with the sword and bow, going on hunting trips in the forest for days on end where I could be alone and think. And then one day a Roman came to visit. He was recruiting for the legions.'

'I've met many Germans in the army,' said Silus. 'Some from conquered tribes that are now part of the Roman provinces. Some from Germania Magna who have joined up for money, or to flee their homeland because of crimes, or just for adventure and travel.'

Odo nodded. 'Travel, adventure. They caught my imagination. We talked, this Roman recruiter and I, and he must have seen something in me. He told me to go to Colonia. But instead of sending me to the legionary headquarters to join up, he told me to report to Oclatinius with his compliments.'

'I know how that works. Then he took you under his wing, trained you?'

'He did. He said he wants me as a scout for special missions. And he told me about the Arcani, and said that if I proved my ability and loyalty, maybe I would become an Arcanus one day.' He looked across at Silus. 'Like you.'

So Oclatinius hadn't held back with this young barbarian. Silus wondered briefly, with an irrational surge of jealousy, whether Odo knew the details of the mission Atius had been on. But he quickly dismissed that as absurd. Why would Oclatinius trust this German and not Silus? Get a grip, Silus. Odo isn't Oclatinius' new, younger lover, replacing you in his affections. And since when did you care what Oclatinius thought or did anyway?

'And how many missions have you been on for Oclatinius so far?'

'Including this one? One.'

How did I know that was going to be the answer? thought Silus. That irritating old man. But Odo's disarming grin made Silus smile back at him.

'Well, get us where we need to be, do as I say, and keep out of trouble. I told your mother I would bring you home safe.'

'Yes, sir.' Odo gave Silus a lightly mocking salute. Silus gave a small tut and turned his attention back to the road.

They were a long way from the Empire now. Odo led them through forest trails, goat tracks around hillsides, open fields and malodorous marshland. He was clearly at ease in this terrain, and knew it well. He explained to Silus that he had travelled far and wide in his time with his mother's kin – it was one of the main reasons Oclatinius had selected him to accompany Silus.

They kept well away from any travellers they saw if they could, but once they encountered a group of four warriors. Young men, about Odo's age, with painted faces, all bearing spears and bows. They were on open ground, a track through a field of vegetables of some sort, with nowhere to hide or to run to. Silus didn't fancy their chances in a fight. He could hold his own against superior numbers in hand-to-hand fighting, but skill with a sword and dirty tricks meant nothing when you were facing down archers with arrows trained on your breastbone.

The warriors approached, with all the cocky assurance of youth. Their language was harsh, throaty, and Silus had no idea what they were saying. Odo spoke to them calmly, and translated into Latin for Silus.

'They are Chatti, and they want to know what we are doing in their lands. I told them you are a trader and I am your guide. They want to know what you have to sell.'

'Tell them if they have coin I am more than happy to trade with them.'

Odo translated and the young men looked at each other and let out low mocking laughs. Their leader, the biggest of the four, well-built despite not yet being in his prime, sporting a long, fat nose, slapped Silus across the shoulder with the back of his hand and pointed to Silus' pack, giving a gruff, incomprehensible order.

'He wants you to show him your pack,' said Odo.

Silus took the pack off his shoulders and began to open it, but Big Nose grabbed it from him and upended it, so its contents spilled onto the ground. Silus protested, but the warrior shoved him hard, so he had to wave his hands to avoid falling on his backside. The others laughed, then rooted through his belongings.

There wasn't much to see. Some cheese, smoked meat, bread and water. A couple of copper and amber necklaces and bracelets, two small cooking pots, some spoons and some statuettes carved in bone. Whatever he had been able to find cheaply in the market in Colonia before he left. Big Nose sifted through it with his boot, leant down to pick up the bracelet, then tossed it aside. He muttered something to Odo.

'Is this it?' Odo translated.

Silus shrugged in what he hoped was an open and placating manner. He really didn't want to provoke these arrogant little shits. Even if he killed them all, their comrades or family would soon come looking for them, and that was trouble he didn't need.

Big Nose then pointed at Silus' sword and spoke. Odo's translation was redundant. 'He wants to see your sword.'

Silus had purposefully kept his blade sheathed and his hand well away from the hilt. Now he slowly took a grip and drew it out carefully. The three warriors behind Big Nose watched closely, two gripping their spears more tightly, the other taking an arrow from his quiver and nocking it, holding the string loose and pointed at the ground, but able to be drawn in an instant.

Silus held his sword by the hilt, between thumb and two fingers, so it dangled with the point towards the ground, swinging gently to and fro. Big Nose growled a command.

'He says give it to him.'

Silus frowned, and looked into Big Nose's eyes. He could see the young warrior wanted to keep his sword, and that wasn't something he could allow to happen. Even if after disarming him, these young barbarians left him alive, how could he complete his mission weaponless? He took in the positions of the other three warriors, their alertness and readiness.

He flicked the sword up, twisting the grip so the point swept in a swift arc upwards. He let go, snatched the sword out of the air when it hit vertical, and swept it downwards in one clean movement so its edge rested against the big vein at the side of the warrior's neck. Purposefully, he let the blade dig into the skin, slicing shallowly so blood oozed along the edge to the guard, from where a single drop fell to the muddy ground.

The three warriors fumbled for their weapons, two raising their spears, though the shocked archer fumbled his arrow, dropped it, and had to pull another from his quiver before he could draw his bow. Big Nose, conversely, stayed as still as a statue, only his eyes moving, flicking down to his left in a vain attempt to see the sword that had cut him. Slowly, he raised his hand to warn his comrades to hold.

'Tell him I said no,' said Silus.

Odo translated into German, unable to keep a smile from his face or his tone.

Stupid boy, thought Silus. This is not a game.

'What now?' whispered Odo.

'Tell him to command his men to drop their weapons.'

Odo did so, and after a moment's hesitation, Big Nose did as he was told. After a brief show of reluctance, the warriors dropped their spears and bows to the ground.

'Now tell him that I could cut his throat this instant, if I desired. But if he gives me his word that he will let us pass unharmed, I will sheath my sword and walk away.'

Silus watched Big Nose's eyes as the German words reached his ears. He saw anger and pride war with fear. Then he saw acceptance win out, in the slightest slump of his shoulders.

'He swears,' said Odo.

Silus kept his blade there just a moment longer, and held Big Nose's gaze. Then he pulled the blade away, sheathed it in one smooth motion and stepped back.

Big Nose clapped his hand to his neck, took it away and looked at the blood on his palm, then glared at Silus. The other warriors scrambled to pick up their weapons, and to step forward menacingly, spears horizontal, arrow nocked and bowstring drawn tight. Silus kept his blade unsheathed, pointed downwards, but ready to be whipped up and into action. Big Nose locked eyes with him, then shook his head and spat. He growled some angry words.

'He says you are no trader,' said Odo.

Silus shrugged. 'Pick up my wares and put them back in my pack, Odo.'

Odo obeyed, getting to his hands and knees to refill the pack. When he was finished he got back to his feet and stood beside Silus, waiting for instructions.

'Time to go,' said Silus. He gave a little bow to Big Nose, and then began to walk through the other warriors, who parted for him reluctantly. Odo followed in his wake like a lap dog. Silus' heart raced as they walked away, their exposed backs to the warriors. He wondered if he had judged right, that these youths were honourable men, not bandits.

Big Nose shouted after him. Silus didn't turn, just whispered to Odo out of the corner his mouth. 'What did he say?'

Odo whispered back. 'He said to watch yourself in these parts.'

'It's kind of him to care.'

'I think it was more of a threat.'

'I did understand, Odo.'

As soon as they were out of sight, they left the track and headed off into the countryside. The young Chatti tribesmen may have kept their word to let them leave unimpeded, but their compatriots would be under no such obligation, nor had he told the Chatti to keep their encounter secret – Silus knew that would have been a promise too far.

So they spent a short while laying a false trail along the track, then doubled back and headed up the stony slope of a small hill. From the top, Silus had a decent view for a number of miles in all directions, and he paused to get his breath back from the climb, pressing his hands into the aching small of his back.

'How far do you reckon?' he asked.

Odo pointed to a row of hills a number of miles in the distance. 'A little way beyond there is where the Teutoburg forest begins.'

'Not far to their destination, then,' mused Silus. 'And no sign of them yet.'

'Did you expect there to be?'

'Not really,' said Silus. He took a swig of water from his flask, went to stopper it, then instead offered it to Odo. Odo accepted it gratefully and drank, then passed it back.

'But it's frustrating. It's impossible to track someone after this amount of time has passed. Especially with the snow and rain since they came this way.'

'Not many hunters know where their prey is going,' commented Odo.

'True. But we don't even know how far they got. Or which of them is alive, if any.'

'We know at least two were captured.'

'That is pretty shaky intelligence, to my mind. Oclatinius wouldn't send me on a mission this flaky if the stakes weren't so high.' He shook his head. 'We're going to have to ask the natives what they know, aren't we?'

Odo nodded. 'It seems so. It's that or go to the chief of the Chatti and ask him personally.'

'Any suggestions?'

Odo scanned around him, and pointed to a small isolated cottage with smoke drifting up through the chimney hole in the roof. 'I guess that would be as good a place as any. If there are local rumours about a band of Roman soldiers passing this way two months ago, then everyone local should know about them by now.'

Silus nodded. 'Probably true. Fine.'

'I'll go in alone,' said Odo. 'If that's good with you, sir. We don't want any more people than necessary knowing there is a Roman wandering the area, regardless of whether or not they believe you are a trader.'

Silus reluctantly agreed, and they walked together to a point a safe distance from the cottage, where Silus settled down against a lone fir tree and broke out some bread and cheese while Odo continued on his own.

Soon the grey clouds opened in a huge downpour, and Silus pulled his cloak around him and huddled under the canopy made by the wide branches. He watched the rain dripping off the edge of the leaves, and felt the occasional fat droplet make its way through the needles to splash his face or neck. He thought back to a time sitting in a Caledonian forest, with rain dripping down his back, scouting a Maeatae stronghold. It not only seemed like a different time, it seemed to have been a different man, watching the approach of the tribal chief, deciding on the spur of the moment to take an action that had destroyed his life and started a war. Where would he be right now if he had taken that other path, the one where he hadn't been a reckless idiot? Probably sitting curled up with his still-living wife and daughter.

He started to shake, and told himself that it was just the cold, that the water trickling down his cheeks was just errant raindrops. He pulled his knees up to his chest and put his face on his knees, and squeezed his eyes tight shut. He became unaware of time passing.

The touch on his shoulder made him cry out loud. He looked up into Odo's concerned face.

'What's wrong? Are you ill?'

Silus wiped the moisture from his cheeks. 'Think I might have started to doze off there,' he lied. 'Lax of me. Any news?'

'Actually yes. An old turnip farmer lived there. Widowed. He seemed lonely, wanted to talk. I told him I was a traveller passing through and he gave me some of his pigeon stew. I asked if anything exciting ever happened in these parts, and he told about how a party of Roman soldiers had chased and caught a young boy, a goatherd, then let him go again.'

Silus' heart beat faster. It was the first time since they had started out that they had found concrete proof that Atius and his party had actually passed this way.

'Where can we find this boy?'

'He lives in the next valley. He should be out and about, tending his goats.'

Silus got to his feet, shaking out the pins and needles.

'Well done, Odo. Let's go.'

Odo held something out in his hand. 'Turnip, sir?'

'What?'

'The old man was most generous. He gave me a sack of turnips to take with us. I think he took a liking to me.'

Silus sighed. 'Dump the sack when we are out of sight of the farm. Come on.'

They walked up the next hill to the peak and looked through the drizzle. Odo spied the herd of goats first, milling about on the slope of the hill across the small valley. A small shelter made of branches piled against each other in a cone shape and tied at the top suggested where the boy might be keeping dry.

They covered the distance quickly, Silus' excitement rising when he saw a wisp of smoke emanating from the top of the shelter. He whispered his plan to Odo, who nodded his understanding. The shelter had a small opening on one side, just big enough for a boy to crawl through. Silus approached it cautiously and crouched beside it like a ratcatcher waiting for a rodent to emerge from its hole.

Odo went to the opposite side of the shelter and after a slow count of five, he kicked in the branches making up the far wall. A high-pitched cry came from within the shelter, and the boy shot out of the entrance, straight into Silus' arms.

He struggled, kicked, even bit, and Silus had a hard time keeping a grip as the boy did his best impression of a feral cat. But this was Silus' best chance so far to find out where Atius may have gone, and he wasn't about to let it slip through his fingers. Odo joined him, and together they pinned the boy down until his efforts ebbed and he lay on his back, breathing heavily and glaring at them defiantly.

'Calm down, boy, we aren't going to hurt you.'

The boy spat and made a comment in German. Silus looked at Odo for a translation.

'He said, "why don't you fucking Romans leave me alone?"'

Silus laughed. 'So he has come across Romans before. Find out what he knows, ask him what he saw.'

Odo spoke some calming words to the boy, then questioned him. The boy looked suspicious, but Odo continued in a reassuring tone. Slowly the boy's demeanour softened, and he looked at Silus, then let out a long stream of words, sentences blurring and merging without apparently drawing a breath.

When the monologue faded away, Odo gave Silus a summary.

'He was caught by a group of Romans who were with a German-speaking guide. He thought they were going to kill him, but instead they made him swear an oath not to reveal he had seen them, in exchange for which they let him go.'

Good old Atius, thought Silus. He would have really struggled with this moral quandary. He wondered if he had made the right choice.

'And did he keep his word?'

Odo asked him and the boy looked shifty, and another fast stream of agitated words poured out.

'He said, of course, but he is lying.'

'Is there anything else?'

'He said that after they let him go, he watched them for a little while. They went that way.' Odo indicated with his arm the direction the boy had mentioned.

'Well, that's something,' said Silus. 'Let's head in that direction and see what happens. Do we need to extract an oath from him like Atius did?'

'He has already promised not to tell anyone he has seen us. But there is more.'

'Go on.'

'He said that not long after the Romans passed through, a band of German warriors came past. Quite a few. He isn't sure how many. Maybe a score. They were Chatti like him, but from a different branch of the tribe, so he didn't know them. And he didn't like them being in his land, so he followed them. They were tracking the Romans, he said.'

'Shit,' breathed Silus.

'And it seems their task was being made easier.'

'What do you mean?'

'The lad saw them stop by a tree, look at something, talk for a while, then move on. He went to see what they had been looking at. He found a piece of cloth tied around a tree.'

'Like a signal?'

Odo shrugged.

'Ask him to show us this piece of cloth.'

Odo spoke to the goatherd, who looked reluctant. Silus delved into his pack and brought out a copper bracelet. The boy looked at it, then at Silus, questioningly.

'Tell him it's his if he takes us to this sign.'

Odo translated and the boy reached out to grab the bracelet. Silus snatched it way.

'Uh-uh. After.'

The boy led them up the hill, around the crest, and down the far slope to a small wooded area. He took them to an oak tree, showing the first signs of budding. On one of the lower branches was small rag, tattered, damp, patchy with mould. It had clearly not been torn accidentally from a passing traveller's tunic, but tied there on purpose. On the trunk of the tree was a carved arrow. Silus tossed the bracelet to the boy, who grabbed it and then abruptly sprinted back the way he had come. Silus didn't even watch him go, lost in thought.

'Someone was giving their location away. They had a traitor in their ranks!'

Odo nodded. 'It seems like it.'

Silus untied the rag and ran it through his fingers. 'Well, if those Chatti used it to follow their trail, so can we.'

Januarius 213 AD

Atius listened closely as Eustachys outlined his mission.

'We are travelling to a place called Kalkriese,' continued Eustachys, 'which sits on a hill near a forested valley.'

'I knew roughly where we were going – I mean which direction and how many days' march – but not the name. It sounds vaguely familiar. What will we do when we get there?'

'We are meeting a German nobleman, by the name of Erhard. He is something like a prince in the Chatti tribe, but was overlooked for rule when his father died, and his uncle became chief in his place.'

'And what do we want with him?'

Eustachys took a deep breath, then told him. The explanation took some time, and Atius interrupted and asked questions at several points to make sure he understood. When Eustachys was finished, Atius let out a long breath.

'Fuck,' he said.

'Quite,' replied Eustachys. 'So, can you do it? It won't be easy for you, I know. You have no training in diplomacy, nor grand strategy. But you are a military man, and I have seen enough of you to know that despite appearances, you have some sort of intelligence inside that thick skull of yours.'

If ever Atius had received a backhanded compliment, he had now, but he was too awed by what he had heard to rise to it.

'Erhard is expecting me, but if you give him the code phrase, he will know you are speaking on behalf of Rome.'

'And what is the code phrase?'

'"Give me back my legions."'

Atius stopped and stared at him. He looked around. They were in a wooded valley, the trees dense on the steep slopes on either side of the road. There was a sudden yelp from behind him and he turned quickly and rushed back to his comrades.

Drustan was holding his foot, and there was a small ooze of blood trickling between his fingers which clutched at a slash that went right through his boot.

'Brigantia's tits, what have I just trodden on?'

As Atius strode over to him to assess the extent of the injury, Memnon bent down to examine the seemingly innocuous ground. He scraped in the dirt with both hands, gripped something, then pulled.

'Bugger me with a pilum,' said Scaurus. 'That's a gladius.'

'Rusty as anything, but a gladius alright,' said Memnon.

'It's certainly still sharp,' said Drustan.

'Look, it's shorter than ours, and the edges aren't straight,' said Memnon. 'They sort of curve, like a waist.'

'Isn't that how they used to make them?' asked Scaurus.

'It certainly looks old,' said Drustan, putting his foot down tentatively. 'Is that ancient thing going to poison me?'

Atius bent down to the ground that Memnon had excavated, and dug around with the hilt of his own sword. In moments he hit something firm, but not metallic. He scooped the cold earth away from around it, and eased the object out of the ground.

The others stared at the skeletal arm, held together by roots that had twined themselves around the bones. It had clearly been severed cleanly through the bones of the forearm.

'Look,' said Memnon, 'there's something else over there.'

Poking up from the earth, covered in moss, only a curved rim visible, was a legionary's shield.

'And there,' said Drustan. What looked like a moss-covered molehill turned out, when the accumulated dirt and vegetation was cleared away, to be a skull. Atius stared at the split down the centre of the forehead, then started backwards as a spider scuttled out of an eye socket.

'What the fuck happened here?' breathed Scaurus.

Atius turned to Eustachys. 'Are we where I think we are?'

Eustachys shrugged. 'It wasn't my idea. It was his. I guess he thought it was symbolic, that it would help his negotiating power to meet us in this place.'

'What are you talking about, Atius?' asked Scaurus in a low voice. 'Where are we? What's going on?'

'This is the Teutoburg forest, isn't it?' said Drustan.

'Teutoburg?' Scaurus rounded on Drustan. 'How do you know about that? You're from Britannia.'

'Everyone knows about it,' said Drustan. 'Especially everyone who has spent any time in the German provinces. The story of Arminius' massacre of Varus' three legions is like a fairy story the centurions tell to scare their new recruits into obedience.'

'Is it true?' asked Memnon.

Eustachys nodded acknowledgement.

'This place is cursed,' said Drustan.

'Too right,' said Memnon, looking into the trees as if German warriors were about to descend on them, or worse, the lemures of their own long dead brothers-in-arms.

'You brought us here,' said Scaurus, pointing his finger at Eustachys and advancing angrily towards him. Eustachys took a step back, hands up to ward him away. Atius interposed himself between them.

'Listen. Listen! I'm as unhappy about this as any of you.'

'Why didn't you know where we were? You're supposed to be a scout.'

'What am I, a historian or something? I didn't know the details of where this battle took place, and I only knew the rough direction and distance of our travel. I was as in the dark about this as the rest of you.'

'So why did he bring us here?' asked Scaurus, pointing at Eustachys over Atius' shoulder.

'That's still not for you to know, legionary,' said Atius, putting his hand on Scaurus' chest and pressing firmly, forcing the wiry soldier to take a step back.

'Bollocks,' said Scaurus. 'We are up to our eyeballs in all kinds of shit, and he is the reason we are here, and you tell me we can't even know why?'

'It's better that way,' said Atius. 'Besides, I've made a decision.'

'A decision? What are you talking about?'

Atius looked over at Eustachys, who nodded once.

'I'm going on alone.'

'You're fucking what?' yelled Scaurus.

'You're abandoning us?' asked Drustan.

'Atius?' Memnon's tone was plaintive, almost hurt.

'It's not like that,' said Atius, suddenly made to feel like a coward. 'It's for your own good.' He realised he was finding it hard even to convince himself. Was he doing this for the mission, or was it because he thought his chances of surviving were better without the others slowing him down? The soldiers looked at him with varying degrees of suspicion and disappointment.

'Look, Eustachys told me what the mission is. It's... big. It's important. I have to do this.'

'So what, we just turn around and march back the way we came?'

'You're not raw recruits. You're not helpless. You can escort Eustachys back to Colonia, and complete your mission with honour. Strike out cross country from here, and with Aldric out of the picture, the Germans pursuing us won't know which way you have gone. You will be back in the baths and taverns before you know it.'

Memnon shook his head and looked away. Scaurus held his gaze, hawked up some phlegm, and spat contemptuously on the ground.

'Let's get it sorted,' said Atius, ignoring the disapprobation. 'We need to make sure the supplies are even so I have enough to get there and out. Let's do an inventory and make it quick. This place gives me the creeps as much as anyone. Come on, move. What are you waiting for?'

But no one was paying him attention any more. He looked over his shoulder to see what had transfixed them.

A hundred yards away, at the end of the path, before it turned a corner off into the trees, stood a dozen German warriors, armed with spears and round shields. Atius turned back to his men, and saw, behind them, a hundred yards in the direction they had come from, another dozen warriors had emerged from the trees to block any retreat.

It was too late to go it alone. It was too late for anything now, but to fight and to die.

Martius 213 AD

They found several of the markers as they travelled, giving Silus confidence they were on the right track, although to be fair, Odo seemed to know where he was going too. The trail led them to an abandoned barn, tumbledown, roof caved in and bearing evidence of fire damage – scorch marks and soot. As they got closer they saw that the intertwined branches that made the walls were peppered with arrows.

'Shit.'

Silus gestured at Odo to stay put, and he approached cautiously, sword in hand. The front door was caved in, rotten planks hanging loose, but he ignored that and crept around to squat beneath one of the windows. He inched himself up and peered in, and once he was persuaded that the only occupants were a couple of pigeons, he returned to the front door and entered.

He knew a couple of months had passed since Atius had been here, assuming he had indeed passed this way, but still he crouched down and ran his fingers around the indentations where men had slept in the muddy ground. He looked around, seeing the splintered walls, split by axes, the tips of arrows protruding through the branches and a handful of shafts littering the floor, and he tried to picture what had happened.

Atius had obviously fought a defensive battle against a superior force here. If it had been an inferior force, he wouldn't have allowed himself to be trapped inside. He closed his eyes, imagining the Germans at the door, at the walls, arrows flying, the screams and cries, the clashes of iron on iron or iron on wood.

There was no blood, as expected after this length of time. Neither had they seen any bodies, or any signs of recent burial. Had all of Atius' men survived this encounter? Had they all been captured at this point, or all killed, and had their bodies taken away for mutilation and display? Or had they all in fact survived and continued their mission, at least for the time being?

The ruined door squeaked on its hinge and Silus started, whirling to face the potential danger. Then he relaxed as Odo came through.

'I scouted around. There is another piece of cloth, a quarter of a mile, roughly east.'

'So they continued on from here, and the traitor in their ranks continued to mark their path.'

Atius, where are you? Are you still alive? Gods, please let him still be alive.

'How far to this Kalkriese place?'

'Less than one day's travel. More than half a day.'

'It's getting late. We'll stay here for the night. At least we will be rested for whatever tomorrow brings.'

Silus settled himself in a corner where the roof was still intact, and closed his eyes. Visions of battle, of rents in flesh and gouts of blood, sounds of anger and pain and death, filled his mind, until Morpheus finally claimed him.

Januarius 213 AD

Atius lined them up back to back, his team, his men, getting ready for their last stand. To his right stood Eustachys, where he felt he could best protect the least experienced fighter. To his left was Scaurus, the least predictable, where he could keep an eye on him. Behind him was the ever-dependable Memnon, and the tough Briton Drustan. They were good boys, he thought. He would have backed them to hold off opposition three times their number.

But that wasn't what they faced here. Two dozen German warriors, stripped for battle, armed with spears, axes and swords. They had closed within ten yards, ahead and behind now, and Atius could see them clearly. Most had a small round shield strapped to their left arm, but their leader, a real giant of a man, carried no shield, just a mighty double-headed axe which he held in both hands His long, tangled blonde hair draped around his shoulders like a lion's mane.

The giant stepped forward, holding his axe at an angle across his chest.

'I am Wigbrand. Chief of these men.' His deep voice, speaking heavily accented Latin, boomed through the wooded valley. 'Who are you to break the peace of this land?'

'I know this name,' whispered Eustachys. 'It's Erhard's uncle.'

'Shit,' replied Atius. 'Do you think one of the others is Erhard?'

'I've no idea. I've never met the man.'

'Speak, Roman. I have little patience.'

Atius raised his voice, trying to match Wigbrand for vocal power and depth.

'I am Atius, centurion of Rome. I demand the right to be allowed to pass unhindered.'

Wigbrand laughed, and a small flock of birds were startled into flight by the noise.

'You have no rights here, Roman, beyond what I grant you. And I say you trespass in my lands.'

'We are here on a diplomatic mission,' said Atius. 'A mission of peace.'

Eustachys gave him a warning glance, obviously worried that Atius would reveal too much, but Atius ignored him. They had little chance of fighting their way out of this. Could he talk their way out instead? Again, he wished Silus was here. Silus would find a way.

'You come here armed for war, not peace. You bring swords, not trading goods. You Romans covet our lands, enslave our people. You don't want peace.'

'We have been attacked. Unprovoked, my men have been murdered, we have been assaulted and besieged. If we had been unable to defend ourselves, we would all be dead by now. And yet, still we ask for peace.'

'You shall have no peace,' yelled one of the other warriors lined up behind Wigbrand, shaking his axe at them.

Wigbrand held up a hand to restrain him.

'Hunfrid here is angry. And he has every right. You killed his brother.'

'I've killed a lot of men,' said Atius. 'You will have to be more specific.'

'His brother's name was Aldric.'

Atius took in a deep breath.

'Well that's us fucked then,' said Scaurus. 'You aren't talking your way out of this.'

'Hunfrid, like his brother, is of our friends the Brukterer. They warned us of your spying mission, and Hunfrid has followed you all the way from the place you call Colonia, with Aldric's help.'

'We aren't spies,' said Atius, but he couldn't keep the note of desperation out of his voice.

'Liar!' yelled Hunfrid. 'Murderer! Come out and face me in single combat. We will see who the gods favour.'

Atius went cold. Hunfrid wasn't as big as Wigbrand, but he was still huge by Roman standards. Atius, even with his Celtiberian blood, wasn't his equal in pure bulk and brawn. Atius was no slouch in combat, but Hunfrid looked like he knew a thing or two about fighting as well, from the scars across his face and chest. He looked at Eustachys questioningly.

'What will it gain us?' asked Eustachys.

'Maybe I can bargain for our freedom if I win.'

Eustachys shook his head. 'The best they will grant is a quick death if you win. And a slow one if you lose.'

'What say you, Roman?' Wigbrand asked. 'Will you trust your life and your honour to your gods, and fight the brother of the man you killed?'

'Do it,' whispered Scaurus.

'What?'

'We're screwed if it comes to a straight fight. And you're getting nowhere with talking.'

He was right. There was little to gain, but nothing to lose.

'Will you grant our freedom if I win?' asked Atius, more in hope than expectation.

'Of course not,' said Wigbrand. 'But at least you will not die a coward's death.'

Atius hesitated. What was the point? But honour was not a trivial issue. If this was his day to die, he wanted to go out like a warrior. And if he did defeat Aldric's brother, then at least that was one warrior less in their ranks, before the battle was joined in earnest.

Atius stepped forward. 'I accept the challenge.'

The German warriors closed in behind Atius as he advanced towards them. Those that were the far side of the small Roman contingent pressed forward to get as good a view as they could. Memnon and Drustan half-turned so they could watch the fight while keeping an eye on the barbarians confronting them.

Atius stopped six feet from Hunfrid and looked into his eyes. He saw no fear, just hatred and anger. Hunfrid carried an axe in one hand, short-handled, single bladed, but Atius knew that it could cleave through bone and skull as easily as a knife cut a sausage, if wielded with sufficient power. And Hunfrid looked to have an abundance of power.

The German carried a round shield on his left arm, covered in hide and edged with sharpened steel. Atius knew that this wasn't just a piece of defensive equipment but was a weapon in its own right. He would have to keep a constant eye on what it was doing during their combat.

Atius himself had no shield – it was an encumbrance too many when they were supposed to be travelling light, fast and undetected through enemy territory. Fighting their way out of trouble was always meant to be a last resort on this mission. He had his trusty gladius, which he held in his right arm, and since his left arm was free, he held his wickedly sharp pugio, a dagger designed for stabbing. He wore a chainmail vest, but was otherwise unarmoured. Again, lightness and speed had been the priorities in his choice of armour. He wondered whether he would regret those choices soon.

At least Hunfrid was similarly unarmoured. In fact, despite the cold, like many of the other barbarian warriors lined up, he wore only shin-length trousers, and from this close, Atius could see the fine patchwork of scars that told of many battles fought and presumably won. Hunfrid was smacking the flat of his axe head across his chest, growling incoherently, working himself up.

'When I give the signal, you will fight,' said Wigbrand without preamble. 'You will continue until one of you is dead. There will be no quarter, no mercy.'

Atius nodded his acknowledgement. His heart was pounding, making his head throb rhythmically. But the fear and excitement washed away all feelings of pain from his injuries, of fatigue in his muscles. A sudden confidence suffused him. What came after wasn't important. All that mattered, like in all battles, was defeating the man before you. He could do this. He was rea—

'Fight!'

Hunfrid rushed him with a roar, and Atius realised he wasn't ready at all. The Brukterer tribesman held his axe high, ready to bring it down in a single blow that would split him in half. But though he was in a fighting fury, he was not careless. A weapon raised overhead should leave the body vulnerable for a swift stab, but Hunfrid's shield was held before him, and in the fraction of a heartbeat Atius had to calculate, he could see no way through. So instead, he hurled himself to one side as the axe came down, rolling over his injured shoulder, ignoring the sudden sting as the superficial wound tore open.

He regained his feet, noticing the warm, wet feeling of blood trickling down the inside of his tunic. They hadn't even made contact yet, and he was already bleeding, he thought. But further reflection was curtailed as Hunfrid swept his axe in a horizontal arc aimed at Atius' midriff. He jumped backwards, and found himself prodded in the small of his back by a spear. The Germans behind him jeered, and one gave him a shove that sent him sprawling off balance towards Hunfrid.

The Brukterer warrior wasn't slow to take advantage, and as Atius fell forward, he brought his axe upwards in a swing designed to bury itself in the depths of Atius' chest cavity. Atius twisted desperately to one side, feeling the breath of the axe, almost close enough to shave his beard. He was falling again, but he had time to slash out with his pugio. The tip merely nicked the top of Hunfrid's forearm, but it was enough to enrage him even further.

Atius rolled sideways, coming upright with his knees bent, ready to spring. He kept the distance to the wall of German spears behind him firmly in his mind's eye as he worked out ranges and trajectories, trying to gauge

Hunfrid's speed and reach. Hunfrid seemed to be making no such calculations as he closed again, swinging his axe diagonally downwards.

This time Atius was able to dodge without bringing himself in reach of the hostile boundary, and kept his balance enough to be able to sweep his sword round in a counter-stroke. The gladius was often thought of as a stabbing weapon, but that was just its main function in battle, where you had tall shields, legionaries either side of you, and a wall of enemies to the fore. In looser combat, the gladius was as effective at cutting as stabbing, and Atius always kept all the edges sharp enough to use his sword as a razor. So he slashed sideways, and although his gladius wasn't as heavy as Hunfrid's axe, if the stroke had made contact it would have been a disabling blow.

But Hunfrid, for all his bulk, had some dexterity, and he fended the stroke away with his shield. Then he followed up by bringing the shield with its sharpened edges round in a sweep that had Atius dancing away again, with no way of parrying. But this gave him an opening, and he stabbed forward, slicing deep into Hunfrid's upper arm.

Blood flowed freely down the limb, dripping from Hunfrid's fingers and the rim of the shield. It wasn't a finishing blow, but it would hamper him. Atius pressed forward, sweeping a low cut towards Hunfrid's legs, forcing him to lean across to his right to block with his shield, which momentarily exposed his left side and put his axe out of action. Atius slashed with his pugio and it bit deep into the muscle of Hunfrid's upper thigh.

Hunfrid howled and swept his shield sideways. Although the sharp edge didn't make contact, the front face caught Atius under the chin, snapping his jaw shut with an impact that staggered him. He wobbled, feeling the ground spin under his feet, forcing himself not to pass out by sheer willpower.

Hunfrid took a step forward, axe raised, but his injured leg buckled and he had to throw his hands out to the sides to steady himself. Atius took a deep breath and widened his stance, planting his feet as the dizziness receded. Hunfrid advanced again, but he was limping badly, and Atius was able to step out of reach to give himself time to recover. The German crowd howled derisively as he kept out of reach of his opponent, but he could also hear shouts of encouragement from Memnon, Drustan and Scaurus.

'Kill that fucker! Gut him, Atius!'

Atius circled, backing away as Hunfrid staggered towards him, cursing and challenging in furious German. Atius knew now he would just need to bide his time. As his own strength recovered, from the blow to his head and the exertion, Hunfrid's would ebb away in red rivulets down his thigh and arm. Even as he watched, Hunfrid slowed, head drooping.

A German warrior stepped from the line and pushed Atius forward.

'Finish him, Roman.' Wigbrand's voice was deep and commanding. 'Let him die like a man.'

Atius hesitated, then took a step forward, ready to deliver a killing thrust.

But Hunfrid, for all his anger, had shown cunning too, and was not as weak as he had seemed. As Atius came close, Hunfrid threw himself forward, wrapping his arms around Atius' torso and bowling him over. Atius fell on his back and the heavy German landed with his full weight on Atius' chest, making his ribs howl, at least two cracking, and all the air was squashed from his lungs.

Atius' sword flew from his hand, skittering out of reach. The straps on Hunfrid's shield broke and it rolled away before coming to rest in an ever-decreasing circle, like a spun coin. Still, he kept his grip on the axe, but lying against Atius as he was, it was impossible to bring it to bear. The German put his injured shield arm beneath him, trying to push himself upright. Atius, seeing the danger, wrapped his sword arm around Hunfrid's neck, hugging him close. The German's meaty breath wafted around him. He tried desperately to suck air back into his lungs, fighting against both the winding and Hunfrid's bulk. Hunfrid struggled against him, and Atius knew that if he got into a kneeling position over him, he was finished.

Panic washed over him as he felt his air supply dwindling, a crushing, suffocating feeling. But through the panic, he became aware of his left hand. It still gripped the pugio.

Hugging Hunfrid tighter, Atius plunged the dagger into his kidneys. Hunfrid's head snapped back, his mouth opening as he let out a howl. But Atius wasn't going to give him any chances. He took the dagger out and thrust it back, again and again, frenzied stabs between ribs and into soft organs, until Aldric's brother slumped forward and was still.

Atius closed his eyes and concentrated on heaving air back inside him. The weight was suddenly lifted from him, and he looked up into Wigbrand's eyes.

'You fought well, and with honour, Roman.'

For a moment, a sprout of hope germinated inside Atius. Wigbrand stamped on it.

'Would you like a clean death, here and now, at my hands? Or would you like to return to your men and die in battle?'

Atius didn't answer at first, just breathed. Then he extended his hand. Wigbrand looked at it thoughtfully, then nodded and hauled him to his feet.

'You understand what you are doing?' asked Wigbrand. 'If you go back to your men now, and I take you alive, your death will be slow and dirty and lacking in honour?'

Atius bent down to retrieve his sword and turned to face Wigbrand. For a moment, he wondered whether to plunge his dagger into the giant chief's throat. He saw in Wigbrand's eyes that the chief knew what he was thinking. A smile played at the corner of the giant's mouth.

Atius brought his sword up and placed it before his face in a respectful salute he hoped Wigbrand would appreciate and understand. Wigbrand nodded, and mirrored the gesture with his axe. Atius turned and limped painfully back to his men.

Scaurus clapped him on the back.

'Well done, sir.'

Memnon and Drustan gave muted congratulations over their shoulders too, while they continued to watch the Germans opposing them.

'That was pointless,' said Eustachys.

'We're still alive, aren't we?' said Scaurus. 'It might all be over by now if Atius hadn't accepted the challenge.'

'It's just delayed the inevitable.'

Scaurus reached across Atius and smacked Eustachys around the side of the head, bringing forth a little yelp.

'We don't give up,' he said sternly. 'Not until the last breath has left our bodies. Right, sir?'

Atius nodded, trying not to show the helplessness he felt.

Before and behind them the Germans began to bang their weapons on their shields, slow at first, rhythmic, then increasing in volume and tempo. They let out a low, loud 'huh' with each blow, and as the sound amplified and reverberated around them, Atius felt the panic rising once more. He gripped his sword and dagger, and he thought of all those he cared for. The list wasn't long, he realised with dismay. His mother. His lover, Menenia, though she had left him. Silus.

Had he wasted his life? Had he been a good person? Would Christos accept him into his father's kingdom when it was over?

The banging on shields became an overwhelming rattle, the vocal noises a roar. Then it all stopped, and the forest path was silent. Not even a bird sang.

'It's been an honour serving with you all,' said Atius. 'Now brace yourselves. Here they come.'

Chapter Seven

Martius 213 AD

Silus felt anxious in a way that was new to him. When he had been serving in the north of Britannia, he had known his way around the enemy territory. Even though the barbarian Caledonians and Maeatae could be dangerous and terrifying, they were familiar, and he had grown up with them on his doorstep. The big cities he had explored, Rome, Syracuse, Alexandria, had been extraordinary and magnificent and bizarre, but they were within the Empire, populated in theory at least by friendly inhabitants.

Here everything was strange. The trees were taller, more angular. The birds sang different melodies and the flowers displayed unusual shapes and colours. And the peoples of this land spoke languages completely alien to him.

So he found himself completely reliant on Odo, and he didn't like that one bit. Fortunately, he trusted this likeable German, and he found himself opening up to him more and more as they journeyed on.

It was Odo's ears that saved them. Silus was venting his spleen about the Praetorian Guard, how over-trained, over-polished and over-paid they were, and how he wouldn't trust them in a fight or with the Emperor's life, when Odo stopped abruptly and held out a hand. Silus was instantly silent and on alert. They were on a winding road that ran between lightly wooded slopes, and Silus scanned the trees for whatever it was that had alarmed Odo.

But the guide pointed ahead and cupped his hand to his ear. Silus did likewise. It was amazing what a difference that simple manoeuvre made to the clearness of sound, cutting out the rustle of the wind in the trees and the birdsong. He heard voices, which Odo's youthful hearing had picked out even over Silus' chatter and their marching feet.

Silus indicated the trees, and they darted off the road and dived behind a fallen trunk a score of yards from the road. They sat with their backs to the trunk, listening intently as the voices grew nearer. There were maybe two or three main speakers doing the talking, but that meant nothing regarding their overall numbers. Instead, Silus tried to work out the number of people from the footfalls. He estimated somewhere between four and six in total, but he couldn't risk a look to confirm. The early spring foliage was too sparse and the tree density too low to provide good cover. Only the tree trunk kept them concealed.

The voices approached their closest point, and Silus kept everything still, breathing through his open mouth to avoid any stertorous noise from his previously broken nose. It had healed somewhat wonky, and was wont to whistle when he breathed in deeply, much to Atius' amusement.

He should have been able to hear their chatter and their footsteps receding into the distance now, but then he realised that the voices were getting no quieter and the noise of boot on stony road had stopped. There were a few comments and some laughs. Silus looked questioningly at

Odo. Odo put his hand to his groin, miming, and Silus frowned, then sighed silently as he understood.

Two of the Germans left the road and walked a short distance into the woods. Carefully, Silus moved his hand onto the hilt of his sword. He tensed, preparing to spring to battle, readying himself to let out a disorienting roar to confuse the enemy and help him take full advantage of the surprise.

But the Germans stopped, each picking a tree around a dozen feet from the fallen trunk. He heard the patter of two streams of liquid hitting the leaf litter, and the two Germans continued to chat as they urinated.

They had surely been drinking, he thought, given how long they pissed for. But after what seemed like an eternity, the flow stopped, and they walked away. Once they had rejoined their comrades, the whole party traipsed off.

Silus risked a peek over the tree trunk once he had gauged they had gone a reasonable distance. There were five of them, two carrying a deer slung upside-down from a pole. A small hunting party. None were looking back, and he watched them disappear around the corner and out of sight before he let himself relax.

'Well done,' he said to Odo. 'You have sharp ears.' He got up stiffly, and held out a hand, but Odo just sprang to his feet with a grin.

'Thanks, old man,' he said.

Silus sneered, then grinned back.

'Let's move on.'

His light mood quickly evaporated. The trees on either side of the road grew denser, and Silus' feelings of anxiety and dread mounted. He peered into the dark under-growth, his mind making patterns from branches and rocks to form images of wolves and bears, barbarian warriors, even demons and other evil spirits leering out at him. Every rustle from the branches, every sudden movement of a bird or rodent in the loam made him start, then shake himself.

Even Odo became withdrawn, his mouth no longer set in a perpetual smile, but a tight line.

'We're right in the depths of the Teutoburg forest now,' said Odo.

'I figured. You know what happened here, I guess?'

Odo looked grim, a strange, almost comical expression on his young face. 'Many tribes say it was a great victory. The Chatti, the Cherusci, the Bructeri, even some of my own tribe. Mostly younger members.'

'You don't see it as a victory?'

Odo spat. 'It was a betrayal. Arminius had sworn loyalty to Varus. He had been made a Roman citizen, an equestrian. He even served in the Roman army in Illyria. Then he turned on them, secretly, shamelessly. Slaughtered his comrades who he had drunk with, eaten with, fought with. He was a man with no honour.'

Silus looked at him in surprise. The light-hearted young man had hidden depths.

'You take an oath seriously,' said Silus.

Now it was Odo's turn to look taken aback. 'Doesn't every man of worth? Don't you?'

Silus thought of oaths he had made that he had failed to keep.

'Of course. But sometimes, life gets… complicated.'

Odo turned away from him, striding ahead, and they walked in silence for some way. Silus knew Odo was disappointed in him, but didn't know what to say to make it right. It was easy to make an oath, but sometimes circumstances beyond your control made it hard to keep it. Maybe Odo would understand that one day.

Silus was so lost in his thoughts that he nearly bumped into Odo's back when he halted suddenly. His hand went straight to his sword.

'What is it?' He stepped around the young guide and looked at the stretch of road that had appeared in front of them after they had rounded a sharp corner. His hand flew to his mouth.

'Oh no.'

Januarius 213 AD

The charging Germans hit them like a mighty wave on the shore. It would have bowled them over backwards in the first impact, and they would have been finished in an instant, if it wasn't for the fact that the charge from behind Atius hit at the same moment. As it was, it felt like a heavy door had swung open in a strong wind, and smacked him against a wall.

With no shields, they had to brace with shoulders against the German shields, and use their swords to fend off the German weapons. Atius had considered thinning them out with a volley of arrows before the charge, but with only two bows it would have been pathetic, easily fended off by the German shields, and would have meant the Roman archers having to quickly swap weapons as the Germans charged.

The only advantage they had was the lack of space for the Germans to use their superior numbers. Back to back, the Romans fought savagely against their opponents. A spear stabbed in by a short, stocky barbarian went through the gap between Atius and Scaurus. Atius chopped down on it so its trajectory angled to the ground, so it didn't continue through to Drustan and Memnon behind him. Then a sword thrust came towards Eustachys' neck, and Atius deflected it with his pugio.

Scaurus caught an axe swing on his own blade, and for a moment he stood eye to eye and toe to toe with his opponent, spitting enraged abuse into the bigger German's face. Then Scaurus brought his head forward sharply, breaking his opponent's nose. The German staggered back. Scaurus pulled his sword arm back, thrust forward into the German's guts, twisted and withdrew. The German fell to his knees, then forward, clutching hopelessly at his rent abdomen. But another warrior instantly filled his place.

Atius fended off another sword swing aimed at Eustachys, then brought his dagger round into his attacker's neck. The German gurgled blood from the gash. He gripped the blade desperately, and as he fell, the knife still in him, he ripped it out of Atius' hand.

Atius cursed, but another German was already before him, and he had to put the loss from his mind. This one, a lean youngster, was armed with a spear, and he stabbed it straight towards Atius' face. It was a mistake born from inexperience. It was simple for Atius to duck beneath the thrust and stab his sword into the lad's exposed middle. The boy's eyes went wide with shock, and he slumped to his knees, mouth open. Atius kicked him in the chest so he toppled away, tripping up the next German who was scrambling to get to them, who slipped in the guts and blood that was forming a slick at their feet.

Given a moment's respite, Atius turned to see Scaurus tackling two barbarians at once, one bearing a spear and the other a sword. He was leaking blood from a small wound on his forehead and a deeper one from somewhere beneath his mail shirt. Atius parried a sword thrust that was about to skewer Scaurus from side to side. Scaurus had no time for thanks, just used the advantage to slice halfway through the spearman's forearm, which dangled at an unnatural angle, spurting arterial blood into the air. Atius turned to his right just in time to see Eustachys desperately fending off a German carrying a huge club. The barbarian swung at Eustachys' head as Atius brought his sword round, slicing into the muscles of his enemy's thigh. It was too late. Even though Eustachys ducked, even though the German was falling, the club still smacked into the side of Eustachys' head, and his legs crumpled beneath him like a bull at sacrifice when the priest takes the hammer to his skull.

There was a cry from behind him, and he turned to see Drustan clutching a spear buried in his chest. Memnon roared in anguish, and slashed Drustan's slayer across the face with such force his sword buried itself halfway into the man's head. It was an error born from anger, since his sword stuck in the bone for just a moment too long. An axe head swept down, the horrifically sharp blade taking Memnon's arm off at the elbow. Memnon stared at the amputation in disbelief, and the expression stayed on his face as the axe swept back and beheaded him.

Scaurus too saw his comrade's death, and he let out a howl of fury and despair.

'Scaurus,' warned Atius. 'Stay with me.'

But the red mist had descended and taken Scaurus' reason. He charged headlong into the mass of warriors behind Atius, thrashing his sword wildly around him. The Germans stepped back, letting him have his head, fending him off at the length of their spears, laughing at his fury and hurling mocking insults at him. Scaurus tried to close on them, but they melted away before him, coming in behind him, closing in on him like wolves around a wounded bull. They prodded him, stabbed, opened wounds. One young warrior, anxious to impress, leapt in behind Scaurus and slashed at his heel, slicing through the tendon. Scaurus whirled and his sword bit into the unfortunate boy's neck, who went down in a gout of blood. But when Scaurus stepped forward again, his damaged foot gave way, and he pitched forward helplessly.

The wolves moved in, stabbing and thrusting, and Atius lost Scaurus to sight.

'Roman.'

Atius turned. Wigbrand was standing in front of him, the great axe dangling from one hand as if it was no heavier than a twig. The other Germans had stopped their attack now, giving their leader space.

Wigbrand hefted the axe into his hands. 'You have fought with honour and bravery. None of your men have disgraced themselves. Now let's end this.'

The audience at gladiatorial games had no idea how fatiguing it was to fight for any length of time. Most people thought gladiators won because of strength and skill, but in many cases it was purely down to stamina. The last one able to stand was the one who would be able to walk home.

Atius was exhausted. The marching had tired him, the one-on-one combat with Hunfrid had drained him, and the battle had taken every last ounce of strength from him. He lifted his sword. It felt like a tree trunk now. It wavered and wobbled in his hands.

Wigbrand stepped forward and bashed it away with one sweep of his axe. It flew through the air and landed on the ground, blade bent almost double.

Atius stared death in the face, and murmured a last prayer. The axe swept round. He didn't feel the impact before the world faded to black.

Martius 213 AD

Silus stared in horror. He couldn't bring himself to move for what seemed an age. The world disappeared around him, so all he could see was those three bodies, nailed to the trees. It seemed like he couldn't breathe, and he found himself gasping uncontrollably for air.

Odo put a hand on his shoulder and he jerked away from the touch. But it broke the spell. Silus took a step forward, another, not wanting to confront what was before him, but unable to look away.

Whoever had put the corpses on display had chosen three large oak trees that lined the road. Maybe they had some religious significance to the German priests or priestesses. Silus didn't care. The bodies had been stripped of most armour and clothing, but each wore a legionary's helmet, making them unmistakably Roman.

The scavengers had done their work. Foxes would have taken the meat from the feet and lower legs, as high up as they could reach. Carrion birds would have pecked away at all the soft parts within reach of a perching point. Flies would have laid their eggs inside body cavities, so maggots consumed the remaining tissue, before turning into new flies and repeating the process.

A large rook with a long bill regarded Silus from atop one of the helmets, refusing to move as he approached until Silus could almost touch it. Then resentfully, it flapped its wings and flew higher into the tree, from where it looked down on Silus as if he were a trespasser.

Silus looked across the three bodies. Bone, sinew, scraps of skin. Little else remained. Was one of them Atius? Swallowing hard, he forced himself to look closer.

The first one was clearly not his friend. The man was huge, and the small pieces of dried skin stretched across face and ribs were dark in colour. Oclatinius had named and described all of Atius' party to Silus. So this had to be Memnon the Aethiopian.

There was no doubt this soldier had died fighting. The lower half of one arm was missing, only a couple of inches of the two bones below the elbow still remaining, ends sharp, showing it had been cleaved off, not removed post-mortem by animals. Moreover, the bones of the neck showed similar damage, and a spike through the centre of the skull into the tree trunk suggested that the head had been replaced on the body when it had been nailed up.

Silus moved on to the next body. It was much shorter in stature than the first. Many of the long bones were nicked with sharp indents, broken or split. The skull had a wide hole in one side, from which cracks radiated. A spear thrust, probably the killing blow, Silus decided. And this one was too small to be Atius.

He looked at the next corpse. A small voice at the back of his mind told him that only three were dead. There were seven in Atius' party – the guide, the diplomat, four legionaries, and Atius himself. If the Germans had understood the difference between the civilian and the legionaries when they placed the helmets on the skulls, then Eustachys was not one of these corpses. So this last body was one of the legionaries, the guide, or Atius.

Flies buzzed into the air as Silus approached, then settled again. A snail was making its slow way across the bridge of the nose, heading who knew where. The sternum was caved in, the ribs broken and folded into the chest cavity. There were no other injuries, nor were any necessary to have finished off this poor individual.

Silus looked into the empty eye sockets and tried to picture the man who had resided there before, looking back at him. He tried to superimpose Atius' features on the skull, and his heart nearly stopped as his friend's face swum into view in front of him. He blinked away the tear-blurred vision and focused again. The dead man had been tall, but not as huge as the Aethiopian. The sort of build that could have belonged to someone of Celtic origin, from Britannia or Hispania, or even German. That was no help.

There were strands of hair still clinging to the scalp, those that hadn't been taken away by nesting birds. It was strange to think that dotted around the forest were likely a number of nests at least partially constructed from the hair of Roman soldiers. The hair was long and light in colour. That did nothing to distinguish the bodies either.

He looked over the body, the limbs, the fingers. Were they Atius'? He just couldn't tell.

Oh, friend. Am I looking at your remains? Or are you still alive, somewhere in this barbarian land?

He had to hope, but it was so hard. Even if this wasn't Atius' corpse before him, what were the chances that Atius was still alive now, all this time later?

Silus stepped back, feeling the anger rising in him, till it felt like it would burst from his chest.

He let it out in a roar that startled the birds, sending them flapping into the air in a great commotion. Odo stepped forward, wearing an expression of anxiety and sympathy. Silus roared into his face, and Odo flinched, but didn't back away.

'Silus. You must calm yourself. You will announce our presence to the whole of Germania.'

But Silus had shouted out his anger and it abruptly gave way to grief. He sank to his knees, bent forward so his forehead touched the ground, and sobbed out loud wails.

Odo waited patiently beside him until he was done. Eventually the sobbing subsided, and Silus rocked back onto his haunches, hugging his knees to his chin. It was too much. Too much loss.

'I'm sorry for your friend, Silus, but we can't remain here.'

Silus looked at him sharply.

'We need to bury them.'

'We can't,' said Odo. 'It will take too long. We will be discovered.'

'I don't care. We need to do this.'

'Some of their party might still be alive, am I right? Maybe even your friend? You don't know for sure that one of these bodies is his.'

Silus looked up at the spotty young lad, who was making more sense than should have been possible for his tender years.

'They need you,' Odo said. 'You are their only hope for rescue. We must find them. We must move.'

Silus hesitated. Of course he was right. But if this body was the mortal remains of his best friend, he couldn't leave him like this. He got stiffly to his feet.

'Help me get them down and take care of them. It will be quicker with two. I will not leave here until this is done.'

Odo looked into his eyes and saw there was no shaking him. He nodded. 'This place is ill-omened. Please, let's be quick.'

—

They left the body that could have been Atius till last. It wasn't hard to scrape out shallow graves in the muddy, loamy forest floor beside the road, using sword hilts and branches as shovels, and the flesh-stripped corpses were much lighter than a freshly dead body. Still, Silus was sweating by the time he had finished digging the last hole.

It hadn't helped that as they dug, they kept finding older remains. A finger bone, a belt buckle. Silus quickly realised where they were, the significance of displaying these Roman corpses in this exact place, and when he looked at Odo, he realised that the young Alamanni knew too. They carried on their task wordlessly.

He walked over to the final tree, and used his knife to prise the nails from the wood, hating himself for disliking the way this abnormal use of the weapon blunted the edge.

The skeleton fell apart as the nails came loose, rotten sinews tearing, so an arm that was still weight-bearing ripped free at the elbow joint and dangled as the rest of the bones crumpled to the ground. Silus took the last nail out with gritted teeth, and then Odo helped Silus move the majority of the body into the grave before he came back for the discrete limb.

He looked down at the remains and thought, this can't be Atius. Even if it is his corpse, it's not Atius. If his friend was right, he would be in heaven now, being happy and good in the company of other happy and good followers of Christos. He wasn't sure Atius would really enjoy it, but it beat the alternative.

He filled the hole in himself, refusing to let Odo help with this part. He swallowed hard as the hollow eyes disappeared beneath the soil. Was that the last he would ever see of his friend? He would certainly never see him in the next world. If there was another life, there was no way Atius and Silus were ending up in the same place.

Odo touched his arm lightly, and said in a soft voice, 'Time to go.'

'In a moment.'

Odo looked around nervously. Silus didn't know if it was the violence, the presence of recent death, the ill-fated location, or a real sense of danger that was perturbing him. He felt it himself, but he couldn't leave without doing one last thing for his friend.

He knelt beside the grave, bowed his head, closed his eyes, and prayed.

He had seen Atius do this plenty of times, but had never paid much attention. What was it he said?

He spoke the words he could remember as best as he could.

'Father in heaven. Holy is your name. Come to the Empire and… do what you want. Give us our food. And forgive us for… all the bad stuff.' What did he say at the end? 'Amen.'

Then he gave the possible body of Atius his own blessing.

'If it's you, old friend, I hope you are with your God. I hope you went easy. I'm sorry we parted ways, that I wasn't here for you at the end. I hope you know you will always be in my heart, and I will do everything in my power to avenge you, I swear by Jupiter, by Mithras and by your Christos.'

He kept his eyes closed, feeling the words bring him a surprising sense of peace and purpose. The only sound was the whistle as he breathed through his wonky nose, and he felt a sudden calmness in the quiet forest.

In fact, the forest was completely silent. Nothing from Odo. No animals rustling nearby. No birdsong.

He opened his eyes, and found the sharp end of a spear about an inch from his left eye. He looked up the shaft to the tangle-bearded barbarian warrior at the other end, then across to others who held Odo's arms behind his back, and a knife to his throat.

Oh fuck.

Chapter Eight

Martius

This one didn't frighten him. Yes, he was big, he was sadistic and when he smiled, a rotten stench emanated from his broken teeth and red gums. But he didn't know what he was doing.

Punching a man in the abdomen hurt. Smacking his face hard enough to whip his head round hurt. Thumping him on the chin so his lower jaw clanked into his upper jaw, the blow reverberating his skull, that hurt too. But it didn't scare him. And that's what they needed to do to get him to tell them what he knew.

The one who actually scared Atius was the young priestess. If he hadn't been in so much pain, starving and thirsty, he might have found her alluring. Intellectually, he knew her oval face and high cheekbones and supercilious expression would have attracted him greatly in other circumstances. But when she took one of the smallest knives he had ever seen, and stroked it along his lower eyelid, or up the inside of his thigh, his bowels tried to loosen, and once, to his shame, he even let out some piss which trickled warmly down his legs and puddled on the ground.

But he was lucky. Their German captors had quickly worked out which of their two captives was the important one, and the priestess had largely left Atius alone, abandoning him to the attentions of the large warrior who kept him softened up.

It was Eustachys who was having the really hard time.

Atius had come round after the battle to find himself bound hand and foot, gagged, blindfolded and slung over the back of a horse. Consciousness returned only gradually and for a long moment he had no recollection of how he had got there. Slowly, the memory of the battle had returned, then the miserable recollection of the deaths of his team, Drustan, Memnon, Scaurus, one after the other. Then the giant chieftain, he couldn't remember his name, confronting him. But after that there was nothing. He had no idea how he had survived.

The horse had stopped and he had been dumped from its back. With hands tied he wasn't able to cushion his fall, and he thought for an instant that the impact had dislocated his shoulder. His blindfold had been removed, and he had been hauled to his feet, and found he was in a large settlement with mainly wooden roundhouses and one large stone building. A crowd of barbarians had gathered round to stare; men, women and children.

He then discovered that Eustachys had also survived the battle. He too was thrown from the horse, and Atius watched him blinking as he adjusted to the light as his blindfold was also removed. He had cuts and bruises around his face and arms, but seemed to have taken no major injuries. He had focused on Atius, and they had given each other nods and grim smiles as each discovered they were not the sole survivor.

Then they had been led to the stone building and separated. Atius had been taken to a small room where he had been tied to the wall, and where he had been, by and large, ever since. He didn't know exactly where Eustachys was, just that he was far enough away that they couldn't talk, but near enough that Atius could clearly hear his screams.

Atius looked at the man before him steadily. He was of typical Germanic build, tall, well-muscled, and he was still in his youth. The first time they had met, he had been introduced by the little priestess as Friduric, a cousin of Aldric and Hunfrid, and she had made it clear how delighted he was to be looking after him.

For the beatings, his wrists were tied and hoisted into the air by a rope slung over a roof beam. It made breathing hard after a time, which was almost as uncomfortable as the punches and kicks. He had no idea how long they lasted, usually until Friduric had worked up a sweat and had had enough. Then they would leave him to heal for two or three days, before working him over again. Since Friduric didn't speak a word of Greek or Latin, if the object of the exercise was to obtain information, it was entirely pointless.

Of course, that wasn't the reason Friduric beat him. It was pure and simple revenge for the deaths of his cousins. But he was clearly not allowed to take it too far. He was not to inflict any injuries that could be fatal or permanently disabling.

Early in his captivity, Wigbrand had come to see him. Then, and at every subsequent visit, the Chatti chief had treated him with respect. His Latin was accented but fluent, making conversation easy.

Atius' initial tactic had been to refuse to engage with his captor, and Wigbrand had taken his silence with equanimity, shrugging and leaving him alone. The beatings had started soon after, but when Wigbrand returned he showed no anger or even resentment. Atius was provided with enough stale bread and water to stay alive, but when Wigbrand visited he brought beer and meat. He always consumed it thankfully, intent on keeping up his strength as best he could.

In the first days of his captivity, his thoughts were constantly on escape. He tested his ropes, he scraped at the iron wall fastenings, he tried to slip his hands through the bindings or untie the knots. He had been in worse situations before, he told himself, and things had always turned out for the best.

But when it was clear that he could not free himself, and when he reflected realistically on his situation – he was deep in Germania, and no friends or allies knew where he was, or even that he was alive – despair set in. He thought about how this would end. Continued torture, until his body weakened and he died? Sacrifice by the priestess to their pagan gods?

That was when he decided to kill himself.

There were few options. Nothing sharp. He had wrapped the rope around his neck, and pulled tight, held it until the room span and darkness closed in.

It turns out that when you pass out from self-strangulation, you stop strangling yourself and you wake up. Actually hanging himself was not an option, since his bonds would not allow him to lift his body off the floor. He tried refusing food. His captors did nothing to force him to eat. When he left the bread untouched, they simply shrugged and took it away. He lasted about two days, before the hunger pangs got the better of him.

At that point, despair gave way to a fatalistic resolve. He would survive, for as long as possible. And he would pray, for release in this world, or for mercy in the next.

He was praying at that instant, his eyes closed, as Friduric pummelled his ribs. The German was grunting with exertion as the rapid blows landed in quick succession. Atius could feel every punch, but at the same time mouthed the words of the prayer that Christos had taught his followers, over and over. 'Father in heaven, your name be hallowed.'

When Friduric stepped back, breathing hard, Atius slumped in the irons suspending him. Friduric spat in his face, punched him one last time, then stalked out. Two other tribesmen entered the room, took him down and secured him back to the wall.

Once, when they had been transferring him from his attachment to the wall to the rope over the beam, he had tried to take advantage of the moment when he was unsecured to try to fight for his freedom. Although he had taken them by surprise, and knocked one down with a double-handed blow, the other had smacked him in the side of the head with the hilt of his sword, stunning him, and doubling the size of the bruise there. After that, the priestess had come to talk to him. Caressing his skin with her tiny knife, she explained why it would be a bad idea to attempt escape again. Then she had left, and moments later, the screams from Eustachys were renewed.

Atius sat with his back to the wall, breathing through his nose, resisting the urge to prod and poke the bruised areas of his ribs and abdomen. He didn't think anything was broken this time. More than once, in previous beatings, he had felt a rib crack, and a deep breath or a cough still hurt like hell.

The hours of the day were hard to judge, since although there was a small window in the room the sky was so often grey, he could rarely tell the sun's position.

Visits from Friduric, the priestess, Wigbrand, or even his guards bringing food were irregular, and did nothing to help him work out the time. So the day-night cycle was his only chronological yardstick, and even that was becoming a blur. How many days had he been in captivity now? Thirty? Forty?

It was taking its toll. He had seeping sores around both wrists where the ropes chafed. His entire body was a patchwork of fresh blues and purples mixed with older yellowy-browns. There seemed not to be a single part of him that was not either newly damaged or in the process of healing. And despite the supplement to his diet that Wigbrand brought him, it was not enough, and coupled with the immobility from being chained up all day long, he was wasting. They had even had to retie the ropes as he had become thin enough that they were in danger of slipping off his wrists.

The door to his room – he thought of it as a cell, though he was sure it hadn't been designed as such – creaked open. It was solid oak, with no lock, but he heard a bar slide into place on the far side whenever he was left alone. That seemed like overkill given how well he was secured, but they were obviously taking no chances.

Wigbrand entered, bearing a clay jug of beer and a plate of chunks of roasted venison. Atius' mouth instantly started to water, and Wigbrand put the meal before him and stepped back. Atius grabbed a chunk of meat and thrust it into his mouth. He closed his eyes, almost ecstatic at the juices that flooded out as he chewed. Despite the pain from broken and loosened teeth, the meals that Wigbrand brought him were a tiny piece of pleasure he could cling to in this horrific ordeal.

When he opened his eyes, he saw that Wigbrand was waiting patiently for him.

'How's your head, Atius?' he asked.

Atius lifted his hands to touch the tender area.

'I think you cracked it. But my skull is pretty thick.'

'The lump has gone, at least.'

During one of their first conversations, Atius had asked why he wasn't dead. Wigbrand had described how, with Atius at his mercy, on an impulse he had twisted the axe in his hands and smacked the flat of the blade against his temple. Atius had gone out like a snuffed candle.

Wigbrand seemed to enjoy Atius' company. He continued to show little interest in why Atius was trespassing in his lands, and talked instead about battles and tactics. They ran through the fight on the road together, the single combat against Hunfrid, the desperate last stand of the Romans against the Chatti. Grudgingly, Atius found himself opening up to the affable chieftain. They praised each other's strength and prowess, and even gave each other constructive criticism on tactics.

Once they had picked apart their mutual battle, Wigbrand turned his questioning to more general military matters. He had a thirst for knowledge, and while Atius took care to avoid giving away anything he thought might give the Chatti an edge in any war against the Romans, he was quite happy to discuss matters of general knowledge. So they talked about the war against the Caledonians and the Maeatae, of which Atius had first-hand knowledge, and they talked about Caracalla, and they talked about history that Atius had not experienced, but knew well from campfire stories, such as the deeds of Caesar and Agrippa and Trajan. Wigbrand in his turn told him about the infamous battle in the Teutoburg forest – where Varus lost his three legions – from the German point of view.

Today, Wigbrand wanted to talk about Caracalla's second campaign in Caledonia, the one in which he had been instructed by his father to kill every inhabitant of that country, man, woman and child. Atius told him unflinchingly what he had seen, and saw Wigbrand's eyes hardening at the massacre of innocents.

'But this is not honourable,' he said. 'Do your chiefs not have honour?'

Atius shrugged. 'They do what they feel they have to, to protect the Empire and its people. The Caledonians and Maeatae had broken peace treaties more than once. And if they were defeated in battle, but not in their homes, then they would soon be back to fight again. Severus and Caracalla have ensured that the north of Britannia will be safe for a generation.'

'By killing mothers and infants. Your Christos that you tell me of, would he approve?'

Atius took a slurp from the beer as he suppressed a sudden guilt and sadness. Was it fatigue or captivity that made him feel emotion more keenly?

'No,' he said, in a low voice.

'Then maybe your Christos was an honourable man, after all. I had thought him a coward.'

'He sacrificed his own life to save the peoples of the world,' said Atius angrily. 'That is not the action of a coward.'

Wigbrand held up his hands placatingly. 'Calm yourself, Atius. I meant no offence. Your god is so different from ours – he is hard to comprehend sometimes.'

Atius glowered at him, and Wigbrand, sensing the mood change, got to his feet.

'I will leave you now. But I have someone else who wants to meet you. My nephew. I told him about our discussions, and he wants to learn about military matters from you, as I have. Will you see him?'

Atius clearly had no choice in the matter, but he appreciated the courtesy that gave him the illusion of free will.

He nodded. 'Of course. I think I have time today.'

Wigbrand laughed at the weak attempt at humour and clapped Atius on the shoulder, which like most of his body was bruised and painful. He opened the door.

'I'll send him to you this evening,' said Wigbrand. 'His name is Erhard.'

Odo struggled in his captors' arms, babbling in his native Germanic language, yelling and pointing at Silus. An older warrior stepped forward, presumably their leader, and questioned him abruptly. Odo replied quickly, breathlessly, gesturing again to Silus.

The leader seemed satisfied and nodded to his men to let Odo go. Odo rubbed his arms where they had been tightly gripped and stared resentfully at the men who had held him. The leader spoke to Odo again, ending with a harsh command.

Odo nodded and turned to Silus, who had risen cautiously to his feet, the spear tip never wavering from him.

'His name is Radulf. He wants to know who you are and where you are from.'

'What else did he say? What's going on, Odo?'

'I told him I was your prisoner. That you are a Roman slaver, taking me back to the Empire as a slave.'

'You did what!' Silus exclaimed.

'Don't overreact, Silus. I'm supposed to be translating for them, nothing more.'

Radulf interrupted angrily. Odo replied then turned back to Silus.

'He says you are talking too much and wants answers. What should I tell him?'

Silus thought quickly. Odo's improvised lie wasn't actually a bad one.

'Tell him I'm Silus from Britannia and I'm a slave hunter. Tell him I am chasing an absconded Roman slave who had conned his way into the legions to escape his master.'

Odo translated, and the Chatti leader asked another question.

'Why do you think the escaped slave is out here?'

'Tell him I've tracked him from within the Empire borders, that I believe he was out here a few weeks ago in a small party of men. Tell him I can pay if he takes me to him.'

The reply came via Odo. 'How do you know he isn't one of these?' he said, indicating the fresh graves.

'Tell him I just know.'

Radulf looked thoughtful for a moment, then spoke and Odo translated.

'The problems of a Roman slaver are no concern of mine. And as you were enslaving a German, you will now find out what it is like to be enslaved yourself.'

Two warriors approached him and forced his hands behind his back, where they tied his wrists tightly. Silus didn't resist. At least they hadn't killed him outright.

Radulf spoke to Odo again, and Odo replied. Then he walked over to Silus and spat in his face. Silus stared at the young scout in shock as the spittle ran down his cheek.

Odo pointed a shaking finger at him, and spoke in a voice so loud as to be almost shouting.

'Listen, Roman. I'm putting on a good show for these Chatti barbarians so go along with it.'

Silus' mouth opened, then he shut it again, trying to regain his composure, to play the role Odo had given him.

'They are going to let me go,' he said, moving even closer, voice tremulous with feigned anger. 'I'm sorry this happened. I'll do what I can. Now, this is going to hurt.'

'What...' began Silus, his words abruptly cut off as Odo kneed him hard in the groin. Silus doubled over and fell to the floor in a tightly curled ball, his bound hands not even able to clutch the injured region. The pain from an impact in the balls was unlike any other, radiating through his body in nauseating waves, and making him retch. He could hear the harsh sounds of barbarian laughter as he groaned helplessly.

Odo, you bastard, he thought. You'll pay for that. He looked up and saw the smiling barbarian leader clapping him on the back. Odo smiled back, waved to the other Germans, made an obscene gesture towards Silus and then walked away, back down the path they had come from.

Silus looked at Radulf, unable to communicate a word with him, and felt suddenly very alone.

--

Erhard showed some family resemblance to his uncle. Something about the widely spaced eyes, the shape of the nose. There could be no doubt they were related.

He looked Atius steadily up and down, frowning at the bruises.

Atius stared back, thinking before coming to a decision.

'Give me back my legions,' he said.

Erhard stiffened, looked behind him to make sure the door was closed. Then he returned his gaze to Atius, more thoughtful this time.

'I'm sorry,' he said eventually. 'For your suffering.'

Atius did not reply. He felt a sudden surge of hatred for this man that surprised him. He tried to pin down the cause, and realised it was twofold. Firstly, he would never have been in this situation if he hadn't had to track into the depths of this barbarian wilderness in search of this man. And secondly, he disliked the fact that he was betraying his uncle, which in turn made Atius realise how much he had come to respect the chief. Neither reason was rational, he knew, but he still glowered at the young Chatti noble.

Erhard cocked his head on one side, obviously unsure of how to deal with this fearfully battered prisoner.

'What have you told them?' he asked eventually.

'Nothing. What do you think of me?'

In fact, Atius knew that if the young priestess had spent serious time with him, he would have told her anything she wanted to know.

Erhard looked into his eyes, gauging the truth of his words. He seemed satisfied and nodded.

'It took you a long time to come and see me,' said Atius sullenly.

'I'm sorry for that, too. But my uncle sent me away to the north, to meet the Chaucii and discuss our alliances. I have only just returned.'

Atius frowned. 'Were you here when we arrived? Would you have been at the meeting point to see Eustachys?'

Erhard looked sheepish. 'Truthfully, no. My uncle sent me away before that, and would not heed my protests.'

Atius' anger rose anew. 'All this way. All this suffering and death. And it would have been for nothing, because you weren't even here, by the Christos?'

'Keep your voice down,' hissed Erhard. 'There are guards outside the door, and who knows walking past the window.'

Atius simmered down, looking up at Erhard through narrowed, disapproving eyes.

'I don't suppose you can get me out of here?' asked Atius, more in hope than expectation.

Erhard shook his head. 'Not a chance. The guards would not obey me over my uncle.'

Atius picked up the resentment in his voice, a little indication of the motivation behind his betrayal.

'Have you seen Eustachys?'

'I asked. My uncle said that there was no point, he is in no condition to see visitors.'

'I hear him,' said Atius. 'Sometimes for hours at a time. I can't block the sound out.'

'And yet he has not given me away,' said Erhard.

Atius nodded. 'There is clearly more to him than meets the eye.'

'Maybe rather less since Romilda started spending time with him.'

'The priestess?'

'She holds that position in the tribe. As well as taking on other roles for my uncle.'

'She scares me,' admitted Atius.

'She scares me too,' said Erhard. 'She has powers. Once, a man accidentally splashed dirt on her robe, and she cursed him. He was dead the next day. No marks on his body. Just found in his bed.' He made a sign with his fingers which Atius presumed was to ward off evil.

Atius wasn't sure if he believed in her supernatural powers, although he wasn't prepared to rule out their truth. But he knew for sure he was scared of her abilities with that little knife.

'Eustachys was the man with the message, wasn't he?' asked Erhard. 'And yet you knew the code phrase that Festus gave me all that time ago when I was in Colonia.'

'Eustachys passed it on to me. He thought we might not both survive to meet you, and had come to trust me.'

'So, what is it?'

Atius hesitated.

'Well?'

'I'm not sure I should tell you.'

'What!'

'I don't know what you will do with the information.'

Erhard stared at him open-mouthed for a moment.

'You will give me the message, or...'

'Or what? Look at me. How could you possibly make my situation worse?'

Erhard took a deep breath and let it out slowly through his nose, balling and unballing his fists.

'So, what will it take to convince you?'

'Tell me why you are willing to betray your uncle and your tribe.'

Erhard turned away, and for a moment Atius thought he would storm out. He could see his shoulders moving up and down as the young noble took deep breaths to control himself. Then he turned back to Atius.

'Wigbrand killed my father.'

Atius raised his eyebrows. He hadn't expected that. He had instinctively taken the side of the likeable chief against his backstabbing nephew, regardless of Rome's interests, and it took him a moment to adjust to the new information.

'An accident? Single combat?'

'In his sleep.'

Wigbrand. All your talk about honour.

'He murdered him?'

'To take his position, yes.'

'How do you know?'

'My older sister witnessed it.'

'And you did nothing?'

'I was four years old.'

'Oh.'

They were both quiet for a moment.

'Well? Is it enough?'

Atius sighed. 'It's enough.'

'So, speak.'

Atius rubbed his sore wrists gingerly.

'Eustachys was sent here to encourage you to rebel against your uncle. You spent time in Colonia Agrippinensis, right? You are more pro-Roman than most Chatti?'

'I think Arminius was more pro-Roman than most Chatti,' observed Erhard. 'But yes, I saw the merits of closer ties to Rome. Both culturally and militarily. My uncle is typical of how you Romans view us, as barbarians. No appreciation of verse or rhetoric or art.'

'He certainly shows an interest in the Roman military.'

'Of course. War is in his blood and bones. He is no fool, and is willing to learn whatever he can to increase his success in battle, whether it is against the Romans or other German tribes. But he has not seen the other benefits Rome can bring, unlike myself. Nor has he seen in person how foolish it is to defy the might of Rome. I think he fancies himself as a new Arminius. If he can unite the tribes, and bring the Alamanni into an alliance, then I believe he will launch a full invasion. And he will be defeated, to the great cost of all of Germania.'

'Can he bring the Alamanni to his way of thinking? I hear they are close to Rome.'

'I don't know. He can be very persuasive.'

Atius thought about their regular meetings, the feelings of attachment and even affection he was developing for Wigbrand. Was the canny chief just manipulating him? Was Atius actually giving away more than he should? Educating the warleader in the military ways of Rome, to his advantage?

'That's why Festus wants a pro-Roman Chatti leader in place. You.' Or at least a civil war to distract them, Atius thought.

Erhard looked conflicted. Atius could see the temptation there, the desire to both avenge his father and snatch the power. But he could also see the doubts.

'There are many among the tribe who respected my father and owed him their spear. But Wigbrand is powerful, and his position is secure. And if he can bring the Alamanni to him, with all the men they can raise, he would be unassailable.'

'You're right,' said Atius. 'Which is why Festus wanted Eustachys to tell you what Caracalla has planned. And when I tell you, you will realise why I wanted to be sure I could trust you.'

Erhard's eyes narrowed. 'Go on.'

So Atius told Erhard what Eustachys had confided to him. And as he spoke, he saw the already pale German turn as white as snow.

Chapter Nine

The journey took about half a day, during which time Silus was not fed, nor offered water. His hands remained tied behind his back and he had been hobbled, the rope between his ankles not quite long enough to take a full stride. While at first this was irritating and a little humiliating, the awkward gait he had to adopt became quickly fatiguing as he shuffled along, trying to keep pace with his captors. Any time he stumbled or fell back, he received verbal abuse coupled with kicks and blows to encourage him forward.

Fortunately they weren't in a hurry, and stopped for frequent breaks to eat, drink or piss, and though Silus would dearly have loved some water, at least he got to sit for a few moments and rest his aching legs before they prodded him back into motion.

It was a relief when they reached their destination, a settlement with scattered wooden houses surrounding a large central stone building, even though he didn't know what his fate would be. His ankles were raw where the ropes had chafed and he reached down to rub them, but was pushed forward towards the central building.

This was nothing like the romanised home of Odo's family. There seemed to Silus to be little civilised influence here, and when he was dragged inside, his first impressions were confirmed. There was no atrium; the large wooden door led straight into a vast hall. A central fire sent most of the smoke up through a hole in the roof, but enough remained inside to catch in the throat, especially after the clean air of the German countryside.

Benches ran along the walls and a throne-like chair decorated with carvings of skulls and mythical beasts sat at one end. The far wall had several wooden doors leading to small rooms. At the near end of the hall, separated by wooden bars, was a stables with three shaggy horses.

The man on the throne had an imposing height, which coupled with the slight elevation of the chair meant that even seated he looked down on Silus. Silus' captors shoved him hard so he stumbled to his hands and knees in front of the chief. They spoke in their Germanic dialect to their leader, then stepped back.

The chief regarded Silus, stroking his blonde-grey beard, then spoke.

'My men tell me you are a slaver.'

Silus looked back uncertainly. He wondered whether to spin a new lie, but he didn't know what had happened to Odo. Maybe the young Alamanni was still in the company of some of these Chatti, or would return in the future. If he contradicted him, Odo might be put in danger.

So he nodded assent.

'It is a dishonourable occupation.'

Silus shrugged. One of the men behind him smacked him around the side of the head, hard enough to temporarily deafen him, and spat some Germanic words at him.

'My man suggests you show some respect.'

'I beg your forgiveness,' said Silus, trying to sound sincere. 'I am just a humble trader, trying to make my living.'

'Everyone needs slaves. But to make a profession of buying and selling them?' The chief shook his head. 'Tell me your name.'

'I am Silus,' said Silus.

'I am Wigbrand, chief of this branch of the people you call the Chatti.'

'What do you call yourselves?' asked Silus.

'Chatti will suffice for you, Roman. Now why did you come to these lands? Has Rome run out of slaves to buy and sell?'

'As well as trading slaves I hunt them,' said Silus. 'I have been tracking an escaped slave by the name of Atius. I believe he joined the legions, and was sent to these parts.'

'You have gone to a lot of trouble for one escaped slave. Is he worth it?'

Silus thought fast. 'He was the favourite of his mistress. She liked his… attentions, if you understand me. She was most distraught when he ran away, and will pay anything to get him back. If you know where he is, and let me return him to the Empire, I can arrange for you to be rewarded most generously.'

Wigbrand let out an unexpected laugh that was so deep and loud it made Silus flinch.

'What do you take me for? You would have me pass an honourable man to you, a slaver, for mere gold?'

An honourable man? Has he met him? Is he alive? Silus felt a sudden surge of hope.

'You know of him?' said Silus. 'You know where he is?'

A flash of annoyance passed across Wigbrand's face as he realised he had given away more than he intended.

'It doesn't matter. You will not get your payment from your employer, if your story is even true. You are now a slave of the Chatti, and that is how you will be until you die.'

'My mistress will pay handsomely for my release as well,' said Silus, mostly to keep up the pretence. He knew there was no way he was talking his way out of this.

'You're boring me now, slaver. When I feel like it, I will decide what to do with you. For now, you can stay in the same room as another Roman who fell into my hands. He has taken some, what would you call it, punishment, but I'm sure you will have plenty to talk about.'

The hope rose inside him once more. Against all the odds, he was finally going to see Atius.

–

The beating that morning had been particularly savage, for no reason Atius could ascertain. It went like that sometimes, unpredictable as the weather. One day he might be subjected to little more than a light slapping around, the next it could be a furious assault of kicks and punches that left him in agony in every part of his body.

Sometimes it helped to picture the revenge he would take on Friduric if he ever got free. The tortures he would heap on him, while he kept him barely alive. The various ways he could kill him. The Romans had a gruesome inventiveness for inflicting horrific punishments on those they considered wrongdoers. One day Atius would picture Friduric undergoing the traditional punishment for patricide, the ritual of the sack. First he would be whipped, then a wolf hide bag placed on his head and wooden clogs placed on his feet. Then he would be sewn into a leather sack with a snake, a rooster and a dog and thrown into a river, to drown along with the frantic panicking animals. Another day he would imagine him crucified, hung out to slowly suffocate as his breathing muscles fatigued, and carrion birds came to peck away at his living body. Or he might fantasise about being let loose on him in a gladiatorial duel, where he could really let out his anger, defeat and humiliate his torturer.

But today, he couldn't summon up the energy for any of that. He just wallowed in his misery, swollen eyes closed, slumped on the cold floor of his cell. He didn't look up when the door opened, when someone entered and sat on the floor in front of him. His visitor waited patiently, but Atius refused to acknowledge his presence.

There was a heavy sigh.

'You're not yourself today, Atius.'

Atius split his eyelids a fraction to look at Wigbrand, then closed them again.

'You aren't hungry? I brought you meat. This ox has been on the spit all night. We have a feast tonight, in honour of the god Baldr. You have heard of Baldr?'

Atius didn't reply.

'He is the son of Wodan and Frigg. He and Frigg both dreamt of his death, so Frigg made every object on earth take a vow to never hurt him. This they all did, except the harmless mistletoe. The gods all had fun throwing objects at Baldr that did him no harm. But Loki, his evil brother, made a mistletoe spear and gave it to their blind brother, who then used it on Baldr, killing him by mistake. Baldr went to the underworld, where he awaits Ragnarok, the end of days, when he will return to rule over the new world.'

A spike of pain shot through Atius' jaw, a sudden protest from a broken molar. He swallowed down the pain, trying not to show any outward reaction.

'It is rather like the story you told me of your Christos, the son of your chief god, yes?'

'Your barbarian gods are nothing like the one true god,' said Atius, his words slurred by his thick, bruised lips.

'Maybe, maybe not. Maybe they are all the same god.'

Atius resumed his sullen silence. He had discussed religion and philosophy with Origen of Alexandria. Even if he was in the best of moods, he would have no desire to talk about it with Wigbrand of the Chatti.

'I see we aren't going to have one of our pleasant chats today,' said Wigbrand. 'Never mind. I have a question for you.'

Atius looked at him, still disinterested.

'What made you join the Roman army?'

Atius closed his eyes again. It was a subject they had discussed before and he wasn't in the mood to rehash it all.

'You said you left your home in Hispania to seek adventure and excitement, yes?'

Atius' only reaction was a laboured sigh.

'And that was the only reason? You left your home as a free man who wanted to see the world? Not maybe, as a slave, fleeing his master?'

Now Atius looked at him curiously. What was he talking about?

'I am no man's slave.'

Wigbrand held his gaze, then nodded. 'I don't believe you are. How curious.'

'What are you talking about?'

Wigbrand stood. 'I'll leave the meat and beer with you in case hunger takes you later.'

He left Atius wondering what that had all been about.

The door opened and Silus was thrust through. The room was lit by one small, high window, and it took a moment for his eyes to adjust to the gloom. On the far side of the room, tied to the wall, was a man's naked figure, head slumped onto his chest.

'Atius?' cried Silus. 'Atius, is it you?'

The man lifted his head, and Silus gasped and put his hand to his mouth. As Silus' pupils widened and the figure became clearer, the poor unfortunate man's injuries became more defined. His face was a patchwork of fresh wounds, scabs and scars. One eye was missing, and there was a sticky dribble from the socket. He was naked, and patches of skin were gone, excised in neat squares, the meat underneath sticky and oozing. He tried to speak, and Silus saw that every single tooth was a broken stump, jagged and raw. Bloody drool trickled from the corner of his mouth. The stench of rotting flesh was overwhelming.

For a moment, Silus could not even tell if this broken figure belonged to his friend. But after the initial surprise, his rational mind reasserted himself. The figure was too slight to be Atius, too short. The relief that washed over him made him feel guilty on behalf of this terribly suffering person.

'Eustachys?' asked Silus tentatively.

Eustachys' mouth worked. 'K... K...'

'I can't hear you. What are you saying?'

'Kill me.'

The voice was just a whisper, and Silus' jaw dropped in shock. Then Eustachys' eyes flicked over Silus' shoulder and he let out a yelp that for all the world sounded like a little girl scared by a spider. He shuffled backwards along the floor until his back was against the wall, drew his knees up to his chest and started rocking backwards and forward, saying, 'No, no, no, no,' over and over again.

Silus turned to find himself looking down at a young woman with long black hair, dressed in a pristine white robe. Behind her stood two bulky armed guards, yet it was the slight female that Eustachys had his eyes fixed upon.

She beckoned to the guards, who grabbed Silus' arms and dragged him to the wall, where they tied his wrists to iron hoops hammered deep into the stonework. When he was secured, she came up close to him, and looked him up and down. She reached down to her belt, and pulled out a tiny knife with a terrifically sharp edge. She grabbed his tunic with one hand, and he tensed as she brought the knife close to his throat. He gripped his bindings, ready to struggle, to try to rip them from the walls, vain as he knew the attempt would be.

She slashed the blade down, and it sliced through the tunic from collar to hem. Two more slashes and it fell away from him. She did the same to his trousers, and when he was naked she touched the blade to the inside of his thigh. Slowly she drew the edge upwards, as if she was shaving him, and indeed some curly hairs dropped to the ground.

Sweat broke out on Silus' forehead as he watched the blade creep towards his genitals. He held his breath, terrified to make the slightest movement that might cause the young woman's hand to slip catastrophically.

She stepped back, giving a light, musical laugh.

'I think it's too early for that,' she said. 'We've only just met. I'm Romilda, priestess of Frigg. You are Silus. We shall be seeing a lot more of each other. But I have duties to attend to, before tonight's ceremonies. For now, I will leave you with Eustachys, and you can find out from him what I have in store for you.'

She swept out and the guards went with her, slamming and barring the door behind them.

Silus let out his breath explosively, then gasped a few times until he could control his respiration again. His heart was hammering, and he waited for it to slow before he turned to Eustachys, trying not to flinch at the sight of him. He sought for something to say, but words failed him. What platitude could he give to this wreck of a man? Instead, he asked the most urgent question on his mind.

'Is Atius still alive?'

Eustachys' tongue worked in his mouth, as if he was an athlete warming up before a running event, getting ready to perform a great sporting feat.

'Yessss,' he said. The broken teeth made his diction sibilant and his voice was hoarse. Silus could easily imagine that was from all the screaming he must have done. Silus nodded, grateful for this piece of information at least, after the disappointment of finding he was being imprisoned with Eustachys and not his friend.

'When did you see him last?'

'Long time. Weeksss.'

'You were captured together?'

Eustachys nodded, but even that small movement made his features tighten.

'Only the two of usss sssurvived.'

'Have you seen him since they brought you here?' Have they done to him what they did to you, he wanted to ask. He felt bad asking Eustachys to speak, but he needed to know, and he didn't know how much time they would be granted together.

'No. But I have not heard ssscreams.'

Silus hoped that meant he had been spared poor Eustachys' ordeal. Wigbrand had called Atius honourable. Maybe that meant he treated Atius differently than a civilian spy. Or a slaver.

Eustachys dropped his voice to the quietest whisper. 'I have told them nothing, you know. I was trained by Fessstusss.'

Silus nodded. That was good, he supposed. Though it seemed of the least importance right now. 'Well done. You're a brave man.' A damned idiot, he thought. He knew without a doubt he would have told them absolutely everything if he had been through a fraction of what Eustachys had suffered.

He looked around him. Stone walls, iron hoops, thick ropes. He tested the strength of the wall fixings, and they held firm, the effort only hurting his wrists. It wasn't hopeful. But that wasn't what made him despair the most. The thing that most brought his spirit low was that Atius, the tough Arcanus, had been here for around two months, and had not yet escaped.

Silus had completed half his mission – he had tracked Atius down. And despite his fears, had found out that his friend was alive. He now realised that had been the easy part. The second half of the mission, rescuing Atius and getting out alive, might be impossible.

Chapter Ten

The sounds from the great feasting hall reached Atius' ears as night was falling. He knew nothing about Germanic religious festivals, though if they were anything like the Roman festivals they might be as diverse as the number of tribes and the number of gods in their barbarian pantheon. After all, the Romans had their festival of the punishment of the dogs, where live dogs were paraded around Rome suspended from forks, to punish them for their failure to warn of the Gallic attack on Rome, while the geese were celebrated. There was the festival of the October Horse, in which one of the winning horses in a chariot race was killed with a spear, in honour of Mars. Then there was the Lupercalia, where young men ran naked through the streets striking women with thongs made from animal skins, the Floralia, where naked prostitutes fought mock gladiatorial battles, and the festival of the Good Goddess, where men were forbidden.

Of course, the followers of Christos had their own ceremonies, as did the followers of Mithras and Elagabal. So Atius thought that in theory the festival of this Baldr could take any form imaginable. In practice, from what Atius had seen and knew about Germans, he suspected it involved meat, beer and violence.

The smell of the roasting ox diffused through his cell, confirming what Wigbrand had previously told him, and it set his mouth watering again. The angry shouts, sounds of scuffles and fights and drunken songs and laughter suggested that he was right about the beer and violence as well. He settled himself down on his haunches and put his head on his knees, trying to find a comfortable position that didn't provoke his bruised parts too painfully.

The door opened, and Romilda stood framed in the doorway. Atius flinched at the sight of the terrifying young woman.

'My lord has summoned you to join our celebration,' she said. She gestured to the two men behind her, who stepped forward to free him from his bonds. When he was untied, they hauled him to his feet, dragged him out of his cell, and took him to the feasting hall.

The vast room was lit by torches along the walls. A long table ran down the centre, filled with plates of beef and other meats, as well as nuts and berries. The ceilings were decorated with mistletoe, the freshly cut plants dangling from the rafters.

There were dozens of warriors drinking beer copiously, singing tuneless choruses and wrestling. Few women were present, and most of those were serving food and drink to the men or dancing. They were frequently pawed at as they carried out their duties, and they all wore fixed smiles which Atius felt were almost certainly faked.

At one end of the room sat Wigbrand on his high, carved chair, and on his right side in place of honour was his nephew Erhard. Erhard was in conversation with Wigbrand, leaning close to his ears and talking earnestly. Wigbrand was nodding along in apparent agreement with whatever Erhard was telling him. Then he caught sight of Atius, and he stood and roared out, his booming voice cutting through all the noise.

'Atius. I'm so glad you could join us.' This brought howls of laughter from the drunken warriors. 'Come, sit near me. Take meat and beer.'

Atius approached the chieftain, who towered over him from his throne. Wigbrand indicated a seat to his left whose legs were about one foot long, the sort of stool a small child would use. Atius sat down, his knees poking up nearly to his chin, and the warriors laughed anew at the humiliating situation.

A slave girl brought him a cup of thick, strong beer and a plate of meat. He looked at her pretty features and shapely figure and felt absolutely nothing. What had this captivity done to him, that it had even robbed him of his desire for a beautiful woman? He tipped the cup back and drained the beer in one long gulp, savouring the feeling as warmth spread through him, taking a little edge off his aches and pains. He picked up a slice of beef and chewed and sucked on it as best he could while avoiding the most tender of his cracked teeth.

To his left were two other small stools, and when he had swallowed he commented to Wigbrand, 'Are you expecting more guests?'

'Atius, Atius,' he chided. 'You are spoiling my surprise. Very well.' He called to Romilda. 'Bring them out.'

Romilda disappeared momentarily, and then returned at the far end of the hall with two men, both with hands tied behind their backs. Atius squinted through the smoke, trying to make out their features in the flickering torch-light. One was the size and shape of Eustachys, though he could barely walk, and was supported under the arms by two warriors. Who was the other? He was sure that only Eustachys and himself had survived. The figures approached, became clearer. Surely it couldn't be...

'This man says he has travelled far to find you,' said Wigbrand.

'Silus?'

'Atius.' Silus' voice was thick with emotion, but his eyes carried warning.

Atius repressed his desire to jump up and throw his arms around his friend, to hug him while he sobbed out his misery. He tried to keep his voice and his questioning neutral. 'What are you doing here?'

'You know the slave-hunter who is tracking you?' asked Wigbrand, frowning.

'I...' It was a lot to take in, and Atius was not at his sharpest. At the best of times he was not exactly scalpel-like. 'Of course,' he managed to say eventually. 'Know your enemy.'

Silus gave him the slightest nod, and Wigbrand seemed satisfied.

'Sit, both of you, beside my honoured guest. Enjoy witnessing the festivities.' He gestured to one of the serving girls, who brought beer and meat for Silus and Eustachys. But Wigbrand waved them away. 'No, no. These two dishonourable men do not deserve the same as Atius. Fetch them something more suitable.'

The girls disappeared, and returned shortly with two cups of murky water and some rock-hard bread. Wigbrand inspected it, spat on it, then nodded, and the girls took it to the Romans. With the girls' assistance, Silus and Eustachys both ate and drank greedily, in Eustachys' case as best as his ruined teeth would allow.

Wigbrand stood now and raised his arms, and the room slowly settled to something like silence, punctuated by belches and farts and the guffaws they provoked. He spoke loudly, his strong German dialect echoing around the hall, incomprehensible to Atius and Silus. Atius made out words such as Chatti and names like Frigg, Wodan, Donar and Loki that he knew were local deities, as well as Baldr and Ragnarok, that Wigbrand had spoken of.

The warriors cheered and clinked cups, sloshing beer onto the floor and over themselves liberally. Wigbrand spoke more, his tone increasingly aggressive.

The volume of cheering rose to a frenzy. Silus and Atius looked at each other nervously, not comprehending what was being said, but appreciating it was unlikely to be anything good for them.

Wigbrand spoke words in a tone of praise and raised his cup in Atius' direction, and though Atius didn't know what he had said, he nodded his acknowledgement, and raised his cup in return. Silus looked at him askance. Atius caught Silus' look, and dropped his head in embarrassment.

Wigbrand then spoke in a more contemptous tone. He approached Silus and spat at his feet, then uttered some sort of curse. The Chatti warriors howled and made insulting gestures in Silus' direction. Silus looked up at Wigbrand, keeping his face impassive.

Then Wigbrand turned to Eustachys. His words made the Chatti men roar their anger at Eustachys, and hurl bread and fruit in his direction. Wigbrand upended his cup of beer over Eustachys' head. As the liquid trickled over the raw, exposed patches of flesh, Eustachys screamed and struggled against the ropes. The warriors laughed and threw more food and even the odd plate and cup.

Wigbrand let them have their head, and then raised his arms for calm once more. Eustachys' whimpering could be clearly heard until Wigbrand drowned it out by calling for Romilda. The priestess approached Wigbrand

and bowed deeply. Then she turned to the warriors and spoke, her high-pitched voice loud and clear. Again Atius made out the names of the Germanic deities and not much more. She drew out her knife, and the warriors collectively drew breath. They knew what she was capable of with that little instrument, and feared and respected it.

She spoke a few more words, and something in her tone chilled Atius to his marrow. Then she turned, and Atius shrank back. There was a sudden ammoniacal smell, and Atius looked round to see that Eustachys had urinated down his legs.

Romilda moved so quickly Atius coudn't follow the blade as it flashed out. The room was still, silent. Everyone held their breath.

Erhard put his hand to his neck, as blood seeped, then gushed out in rivulets. He stared wide-eyed at Romilda as he squeezed, trying to hold back the flow. He turned to Wigbrand and opened his mouth to speak, but blood poured from his lips and dribbled down his chin. He pitched forward off his chair and lay face first in a growing pool of dark liquid. His body twitched, once, twice, three times, then was still.

The silence persisted, even the drunken warriors, used to fighting and bloodshed, stunned into sobriety.

Wigbrand crowed triumphantly over Erhard's corpse. Whether the German had been sacrficed in a ritual or executed because his rebellion had been discovered or both, Atius didn't know.

The warriors cheered, but whether it was the shock or disapproval, the response was muted. Wigbrand didn't seem to care.

Two of Wigbrand's warriors came forward and grabbed the body by the arms, dragging it away, leaving a muddy, bloody trail across the dirt floor.

Wigbrand spoke in a more upbeat tone, clearly exhorting his men to continue their celebrations.

Slowly, reluctantly at first, but then with more enthusiasm, the men of the Chatti returned to the serious business of getting very drunk. From outside a woman's scream could be heard, which continued as a long series of wails. Erhard's sister, Atius guessed. Wigbrand started a loud song, and the men joined in, and the cries of grief were drowned out.

–

At the back of the hall, eating and drinking sparsely, keeping to the shadows away from the torchlight, a young, spotty Germanic youth observed everything. Presently, Wigbrand signalled for the three Roman men to be taken back to their cells.

Odo watched them go.

–

The guards, who were more sober than most of the warriors, but more drunk than they should have been, led all three prisoners back to a single cell, the one Eustachys had been in. Silus presumed they didn't have the number of rooms to imprison them all separately, and so had decided to lump them in together. There were only two iron hoops in the walls, so they tied Atius and Eustachys to one, and Silus to the other. They slammed and barred the door, and Atius heard the footsteps retreat into the dark.

Once they were out of earshot, Silus opened his mouth to speak, but Atius beat him to it.

'What the fuck are you doing here?'

'Good to see you too, mate.'

'Seriously, Silus. You're supposed to have retired.'

'Yeah, well. Some fool needed rescuing.'

Atius let out a humourless laugh. 'Well you're doing a great job of it so far.'

'Give me a break. I've left a luxurious island in the Mare Nostrum, warm weather, beaches, no one trying to kill me. And I've come halfway across the world on the off chance you aren't dead and that I can find you.'

'You fucking idiot.' He grinned. 'It's good to see you. You wouldn't believe the number of times I've wished you were here.'

'Instead of you, you mean?'

'Ha. You know what I mean. But now you're here, I wish you weren't. I wish you were safe on Lipari with Issa and Tituria.'

'Well, we are where we are, and we need to come up with some way of getting out of here.'

'Damn right,' said Atius. 'What's the plan?'

Silus hesitated. This was the point where he was supposed to come up with something brilliant.

'Um. Have you tried untying the ropes?'

'No, Silus,' said Atius. 'I've been here for the Christos knows how long, being beaten black and blue every day, and it never occurred to me just to untie the ropes. Of course I've tried untying the fucking ropes! They aren't stupid. They tie them dry, then wet them so they swell. And with your hands bound, it's impossible to work the knot free. It takes them long enough when they want to move you for them to do it themselves, with two hands free.'

Silus looked at Eustachys, who was trembling and moaning quietly to himself. 'Well, you have four hands between you now. I can't reach you from here, but maybe the two of you can work together.'

'That's... not so stupid,' said Atius. 'I can't reach my own knots, but I can reach Eustachys'. Eustachys, hey. Give me your hands.'

Eustachys didn't respond.

'Eustachys,' hissed Atius. 'Look at me. This may be our only chance.'

Eustachys started to rock back and forth. 'No, no, no. She won't be happy. It will make her angry.'

The words gave Atius a chill, and he looked over at Silus. 'He's right, you know. If we get caught trying to escape, the priestess will...' He couldn't finish the sentence.

'Are you fucking kidding me? You're scared of that little girl?'

Atius gestured at Eustachys. 'Yes. And so should you be.'

'Pull yourself together, Atius. You're an Arcanus!'

Atius shook himself and gave a short nod. 'Sorry, Silus. It's been... hard. Eustachys, give me your hands. Trust me.'

Slowly Eustachys extended his shaking hands. It was too dark for Atius to see what he was doing, and as he had told Silus, the damp ropes had made the knots tight, as well as slippery. He worked away at them doggedly, and though he could hear Silus tutting impatiently, he kept a steady pace. Slowly, a fraction of an inch at a time, the knots loosened, and then suddenly they parted. Triumphantly, Atius threw the ropes aside.

'They're off, Eustachys. Now, you untie me.'

Eustachys turned his lone eye on Atius and held up his hands. The skin of all pads of all five fingertips on each hand had been cut away, leaving raw, scabby flesh.

'I... I don't think I can.'

Atius stared at the disfigured digits, and looked across at Silus. Silus glared back at Atius. Atius clenched his jaw.

'Eustachys, I'm sorry to ask this of you,' he said. 'But you have to do this. Not just to save our lives. But for Rome. We need to tell Festus that Erhard is dead, that he can't rely on a Chatti civil war to keep them away from our borders. You have suffered so much, Eustachys, to keep Rome and your Emperor safe. Just a little more suffering, and we will be free.'

Eustachys swallowed hard. He reached out and took Atius' proffered wrists, and started to work on the knots. His breathing came harsh through his broken teeth. A whimpering sound came from somewhere at the back of his throat, and the ropes became even more slick with pus, blood and other juices for his suppurating wounds.

But he kept on, and though anxiety threatened to overwhelm Atius, he gave no admonishments to hurry, in acknowledgement of Eustachys' bravery. Silus too was quiet, trying to make out what was happening in the half light provided by the moon when it came out from behind dark, scudding clouds.

Eventually the knot began to come undone. Atius fought every instinct to wrench his hands apart, knowing that if he did so, he risked tightening the bindings once more and undoing all that Eustachys had done. More excruciating time passed, as Atius strained his ears for the return of their guards, come to check on them. But the ropes fell free with the door remaining firmly closed.

Atius gently rubbed his chafed wrists, flexed his fingers to work blood into them to combat the numbness and the pinpricks of pain from his returning circulation. He went quickly to Silus and began the process of freeing him. With both hands completely at liberty, he progressed more rapidly, but it still took an acutely anxious length of time before Silus was finally untied.

As soon as he was loose, Silus stood and threw his arms around Atius, and they hugged, tears welling up on both sides. Atius had to bite his tongue to stop himself from sobbing aloud.

Silus stepped back first.

'What now?' asked Atius.

Silus looked at the window. It had no bars, but was too small for any of them to fit through, even after the weight that Atius and Eustachys had lost. He turned to the solid oak door.

'It's barred?'

Atius nodded. 'I always hear them drop a heavy bar in place when they leave.'

Silus touched his fingers to the door and traced the frame. 'This will come down,' he said. 'Especially if we shoulder-barge it at the same time.'

'And then what? Even over the noise of the festival, they will hear. Do we fight our way out past dozens of drunk, angry Germans?'

'I… don't know. Will we be worse off than we are now?'

'You don't know how bad things can get yet, Silus.'

They both turned back to the door, looking at it in indecision.

Then there was a noise. The scrape of wood on wood and metal as the bar was lifted free. The door creaked as it opened a crack. Silus and Atius moved automatically to either side. Unarmed, fatigued, damaged as they were, they were still Arcani, and they were dangerous with or without weapons, whatever state they were in.

A head poked around the door, and Atius reached out, grabbed the collar beneath it, and hurled the intruder across the cell. The slight figure rolled, gracefully at first, but with such momentum that he thumped hard into the opposite wall.

Silus was on him in an instant, grasping his shoulders, slamming him again against the stonework, pulling his fist back, ready to slam it into the intruder's face hard enough to break his skull.

'Silus, wait! It's me.'

Silus held his fist in place as he stared into the face before him.

'Odo?'

'Who?' asked Atius.

'It's Odo,' said Silus. 'He was – is – my guide. He is an Alamanni.'

'A German? Break his neck, and let's go.'

'Break his… what are you talking about?'

'Believe me, Silus, you can't trust a German. Kill him now, or you will regret it.'

Silus gaped at his friend. Atius kept his face firm. 'I know you're thinking it is my captivity and torture talking, but it's not that. I'll explain later. Just do it.'

'No!' exclaimed Silus. He stood and held out a hand for Odo, who took it and leapt nimbly to his feet. 'You came back,' he said to the young guide.

Odo grinned. 'Of course. I swore to help you find your friend. Besides, you have been a guest in my house.'

Silus smiled back. 'Thank you, Odo.'

'Thank me when we are well out of this place.'

Atius shook his head. 'You're dooming us, Silus.'

'We don't have time to discuss this. We need to work out how to get out of this place without being caught. There are still a lot of warriors out there, and drunk or not, we will likely be spotted if we just walk out of here.'

'A diversion?' suggested Atius.

'Yes, but who, and how?'

'Where's your friend?' asked Odo.

Atius and Silus looked around in surprise. The door was wide open, and Eustachys was gone.

—

They crept along a short corridor between rooms of uncertain purpose, stores or living quarters, they didn't know. Each had a closed wooden door, and they tensed, expecting one to fly open at any moment. Silus considered opening one and seeing if it had a way of egress to the outside, but as the size of each appeared similar to that of the cell they had been in, he guessed their windows would be similarly small, and any one of them could hold a sleeping warrior or servant who could set off the alarm. Besides, Atius refused to abandon Eustachys, and they presumed he had continued onward.

They reached the end of the corridor, and Silus and Atius peeped around the corner so they could see into the great hall. The numerous torches lit the scene well. Some of the warriors were rutting with servant girls who showed varying degrees of enthusiasm, from those clearly enjoying themselves to those who were clearly distressed. Others were arm wrestling, or engaging in drinking contests. As with any drunken crowd, some were being over-friendly, some were angry and violent and some were morose.

But slowly they all stopped what they were doing as they turned to stare in bemusement at the figure who had got up on to the long central table and shuffled along, kicking plates and cups aside.

'Oh shit, Eustachys,' breathed Atius.

At the far end of the table, in the seat previously occupied by Erhard, sat the priestess Romilda, who had been surveying the misbehaving men with amusement. Wigbrand was absent now, maybe away with a girl, maybe passed out, or maybe just content to leave his men to their feasting.

Eustachys reached the end of the table and sat on the edge in front of Romilda. She looked at him and gave him a pitying smile.

'My little toy has come to join us,' she said in heavily accented Latin, and gave a little laugh. But this time Eustachys did not flinch away. 'Could you not bear to be without me?' She leant forward and kissed him full on the lips, and though his traumatised mouth must have protested, he did not pull away. Romilda lengthened the mocking kiss as the warriors roared with laughter.

Then she stiffened. She looked down.

A red stain appeared on the front of her hitherto spotless white robe.

The hilt of a knife was protruding out of her abdomen, just under the ribs, angled so it was clear the blade was buried deep in her liver. Silus presumed Eustachys had picked the knife up from the table, where it had been discarded by a carousing warrior after using it to slice meat into bite-sized chunks.

Romilda clutched the hilt, her mouth open, the colour draining rapidly from her face. The hall fell deadly silent as the confused, drunken warriors tried to understand what they were looking at.

Eustachys made no attempt to flee. He stepped forward, pressing his face close to hers.

'This is for every slice of your knife,' he said, voice calm and even. 'For my eye. For my skin. For every sadistic torture you inflicted on me. I vowed I would watch you die.'

Romilda dropped to her knees, her eyes still fixed on Eustachys. Her robe was soaked in crimson now. Her mouth worked and it seemed for a moment she had no breath to speak. Then she managed to whisper:

'Every single moment... was a pleasure.'

Then she pitched forward onto her front, ramming the knife even further home as her weight landed on it.

The spell that had been binding the Chatti warriors broke. They roared their outrage as one, and rushed Eustachys, who still stood calmly over the body.

Odo squeezed Silus' wrist.

'Now's our chance,' he hissed.

Silus knew Odo was right, though he hated the fact. Then he saw Atius preparing to rush forward to help Eustachys. He grabbed his friend's arm.

'Atius. Let's go.'

Atius watched Eustachys disappear under a pile of warriors, all punching, kicking, biting, tearing, weapons forgotten in their animal fury to rend and kill. He turned to Silus with a look of anguish, but Silus gripped him harder. 'He knew what he was doing. He did it for himself. But he also did it for us. As a distraction.'

They remained unnoticed for the moment, but it wouldn't stay that way for long. Silus gritted his teeth in anxiety, fighting a desire to flee, not willing to move until he knew Atius was with him.

'Fuck them,' said Atius after a few heartbeats which seemed like a lifespan. 'They are going to pay.'

'They will, but first let's survive.'

Atius nodded, and Odo hurried away, skirting the hall, sticking to the shadows. Silus thrust Atius after him, making sure he was ahead of him so he could prevent him changing his mind and running back to help Eustachys. They reached a side door and Odo eased it open, then slid through. Silus pushed Atius through the narrow gap, then took one last look back.

Eustachys could not be seen, but some of the warriors were stepping back, looking around them in confusion. One walked over to Romilda's body and lifted her reverentially. Another swept plates and cups off the table, and Romilda was laid gently upon the surface.

Wigbrand suddenly appeared, emerging from one of the side rooms, his imposing body stark naked.

Silus ran, the Chatti chief's roar chasing him out.

Odo and Atius were already a dozen yards ahead, and he put his head down and sprinted after them, pumping his fists as he tried to put as much distance as possible between himself and the hornets' nest Eustachys had just punched.

There were no Chatti men out and about in the settlement — they were all at the feast. Nor were there any women. Those that the men wanted there were already in the hall, or had been taken somewhere for a warrior's amusement. The rest were out of sight, probably thankful to be left unmolested.

But as they reached the edge of the settlement one boy stepped into their path. He was tall but skinny, and looked to have barely reached adolescence, younger even than Odo. He held a spear before him, pointed forward and levelled at their chests. They skidded to a halt.

'Get out of the way,' growled Atius, but if the boy understood he showed no sign of obeying. The spear tip did not waver.

Odo spoke to him in German, and the boy replied angrily.

'We don't have time for this,' said Silus, looking anxiously behind him for signs of pursuit. There was still uproar coming from the hall, but no one had emerged from it yet.

'Fuck this,' said Atius. He took a swift step forward, and slipped his forearm underneath the spear. With a sideways and upwards motion, he flicked the spear tip away and followed through with a hard punch into the centre of the boy's face. The force of the blow knocked the juvenile warrior out cold, and he lay on his back, eyes rolled into his head, blowing bloody bubbles from his broken nose.

Atius grabbed the spear midway down the shaft and lifted it high above his head. His body tensed as he prepared to thrust down into the unconscious child.

Silus caught his wrist.

'What the fuck are you doing?'

Atius looked at him in surprise.

'He's a fucking German. He deserves to die.'

'Odo is a fucking German too, and he saved our lives.'

Silus wrenched the spear out of his friend's hands.

'I know you've been through a lot, Atius, but you're better than this.'

'You don't know me any more,' replied Atius, and Silus' heart fell at the bitter reproach. But Atius made no further move against the boy.

Odo had watched the exchange with obvious concern, but now it was resolved, he urged them into flight again. They ran for the nearby forest, and the dark shadows beneath the trees felt like a mother's embrace.

But then they heard the shouts and cries from the settlement as warriors emerged angrily from the hall, and Silus knew their escape had been discovered.

Now, it was a straight race.

Chapter Eleven

Running in almost complete darkness through forest undergrowth with low branches, scrubby bushes and roots liberally scattered throughout is fraught with risk. But when you are running for your life, you have to accept that risk.

Odo was light on his feet, his night vision was excellent, and he knew the terrain, so he picked a way through for them that minimised the likelihood of them stumbling, tripping and falling flat on their faces. Silus was fit and fast, and also used to moving quickly through forest from his time as a scout in the north of Britannia, although the spear he had taken kept snagging. But Atius was less familiar with this type of landscape, and furthermore he was far from fit. Malnourished and unable to exercise, the meat had dropped from him, leaving him a mere skeleton when compared to the muscular physique that he had possessed when Silus had waved him goodbye from the shores of Lipari all that time ago.

Still, Atius had willpower and fear driving him on. Though Silus and Odo had to slow their pace to let him keep up, he didn't stop and he didn't give up, even as fatigue started to bite, legs started to burn, breath was drawn in through wide open mouth with great heaves of his chest.

Their pursuers of course also knew the terrain, and were mainly fit and strong warriors, some of whom were also young and quick. They were numerous too, able to cover a lot of ground by spreading out, not needing to pause to track them, just flooding the area with bodies.

But in the escapees' favour, all those chasing them were drunk, which impaired both their speed and their reasoning. So although Silus had heard a lot of commotion uncomfortably nearby at first, most of the noise receded as they retreated further into the interior of the forest.

Most but not all. The quickest, youngest warriors could easily outstrip their pace, and if just one was lucky enough to get sufficiently close to hear or see them, they could raise the alarm for the rest of the tribe. Silus' relief at escaping, amplified by finding Atius and getting him out alive, was rapidly receding as the perilousness of their position sank in.

He too was feeling the fatigue, although he was in much better shape than Atius. His heart was pounding and his breathing heavy. The noise they made as they rushed on sounded in his ears like a charging herd of cows, though he hoped the dense vegetation muffled the volume at least partially.

His foot caught a root, one of those ones that emerged from the soil and then disappeared again, making a hoop. He felt himself pitching forward but his foot remained trapped, and he felt the strain on his ankle as it twisted in an unnatural direction.

He fell, turning at the last moment to take the impact on his shoulder, and his spear flew from his hands. As he came down, the root tore in two, and his foot came free. He took a moment to rub his ankle, and to move his foot in tentative circles. It was sore, but not overly so. He was lucky it hadn't broken or sprained. If he was with the legions, that sort of injury would have seen him stretchered back to the hospital, with a two-month recovery period. In these circumstances, though, the injury would be fatal.

Atius, who had been three yards behind him, stopped and leant forward, hands on his knees, gasping.

'In one piece still?' he said with what breath he could spare.

'Seems so,' said Silus. 'For now.'

Atius held out a hand to help him up, and Silus reached for it, then stopped.

'Listen!' he said earnestly, voice low.

Atius cocked his head on one side, and Odo, who had halted just ahead of them, turned back and cupped his hands to his ears.

'They're coming,' said Odo.

Silus could hear it more clearly now. The sound of someone rushing towards them, breaking twigs and brushing against leaves in their haste. They were about a hundred yards away, he estimated, but closing rapidly. Silus looked at Atius who was still breathing heavily, and made a quick decision.

'Run, both of you. I'll catch you up.'

Atius looked at him doubtfully.

'Go. There is no time to argue.'

Atius helped Silus to his feet, and slapped him on the shoulder, then followed Odo, who was already retreating deeper into the forest. Silus picked up the spear, felt its weight, its balance, and then listened intently, gauging direction and distance. He selected a tree trunk, put his back to it and gripped the spear tightly.

The approaching warrior was showing no sign of caution. The one who found the escaped prisoners, especially the associates of the sacrilegious priestess murderer, would surely be celebrated by his tribe. He continued onwards at full speed, the noise of his approach growing ever louder. But it was only when he was within half a dozen yards that Silus knew for sure that he had picked his ambush location correctly.

His fingers tightened around the spear shaft, willing himself to wait, wait.

Then he stepped out, straight into the path of the onrushing pursuer. Silus didn't even have to thrust. The warrior ran straight onto the spear, skewering himself from front to back. The spear tip erupted from his back in a gout of blood, but the warrior's momentum kept him going. He barrelled into Silus and knocked him over backwards, landing on top of him and driving the wind from Silus' chest. Silus lost his grip on the spear, but it didn't matter.

The astonished warrior's face was an inch from Silus' own, so close it looked like a lover's clinch. He coughed, and blood sprayed into Silus' eyes. Silus pushed hard, rolled him off to one side. He coughed again, gasped, coughed once more, and died.

Silus bent over him to retrieve the spear. The warrior was a young man, about the same age as Odo. Probably unmarried, childless. And now he always would be. Silus yanked on the spear shaft, and it came loose with a sucking sound. Some blood and flesh clung to the tip, and he wiped it on the dead German. Then, with one last look at the still corpse, he set off after Atius and Odo.

–

They stopped when it was obvious that Atius could go no further. Odo walked a short distance back the way they had come to check for signs of pursuit. Atius lay on his back, breathing hard. Silus sat next to him and put a hand on his shoulder. They stayed like that, wordless, until Odo returned.

'Nothing,' he said. 'We're safe, for now.'

'They'll find the body soon, if they haven't already,' said Silus. They had fled as fast as Atius could manage for the best part of an hour, and Silus was confident that they had avoided the initial chaotic attempts by the drunken mob of warriors to catch them. The nature of the chase would change now, from flailing around in the dark, to tracking with dogs and scouts. The corpse of the warrior Silus had killed would give them a good indication which way they were headed. Now Silus needed cunning as much as speed.

But first, Atius needed time to recover. Odo suggested he scout around while they waited, and Silus agreed. The young German slipped away into the trees.

Silus looked down at Atius. Although he was just a grey shape in the darkness, Silus could see his diminished figure.

'What did they do you, friend?' he whispered, as much to himself as to Atius. Atius didn't reply, but his breathing slowed, and after a while he levered himself up until he was sitting upright.

'The boy,' he said. 'What did you call him? Odo?'

'That's right.'

'What do you know about him?'

Silus frowned, though Atius would not be able to see his expression.

'What do you mean?'

'How did he come to be your guide? What's his background? What's his allegiance?'

'Why are you asking? What's wrong?'

Atius grasped Silus' upper arm and spoke with urgency. 'Tell me, quickly, before he returns.'

'Oclatinius assigned him to me. He is Alamanni, and they are no enemies of Rome.'

'How do you know this?'

'That he is Alamanni? I met his family.'

'No, that they are not Rome's enemies.'

'I...' He didn't know, of course. Even if he had been on active service these past months, he would not have been privy to the meetings and ever shifting treaties, pacts and alliances that constituted Roman diplomacy.

'I trust him,' said Silus eventually.

'With your life?' asked Atius.

Silus opened his mouth to reply, but at that moment Odo returned. He'd made so little noise on his approach, he took Silus by surprise, who wondered if he had been listening to their conversation. But his voice was light and unconcerned when he spoke.

'There is a stream a short distance further on. I filled my water bottle, and I found these mushrooms growing there. Eat them.'

Silus took a handful, turned them over to inspect them, and sniffed them. He was used to eating fungi when he was on foraging while on scouting missions in Britannia, but these were unfamiliar. Odo offered some to Atius, but he made no move to accept them.

'You first,' said Atius gruffly.

Odo shrugged, and shoved a couple in his mouth, chewing and swallowing. Silus did likewise. Atius still hesitated. Silus couldn't understand what was wrong with him. He needed all the nutrition he could get.

'Eat, Atius. They aren't much, but they are better than nothing.'

Reluctantly, Atius took a few of the mushrooms and chewed them slowly and suspiciously before swallowing. Silus saw Odo looking at Atius, but he couldn't read his expression in the dark. An uneasy feeling grew inside him. The last thing he needed was conflict between those two.

'Atius, are you fit? Can you go on?'

'Of course,' said Atius, and struggled to his feet, waving away Odo's offer of help.

'Right, Odo, lead us to that stream. We'll walk along it for a while to throw off any dogs they use, then I want you to lead us north for a while.'

'North?' Atius sounded puzzled. 'The quickest way to the border is due west.'

'Exactly,' said Silus. 'So which way do you think they will assume we are going?'

Atius was quiet for a moment. Then he said, in a low voice, 'I've missed you, Silus.'

Silus clapped him on the back. 'Let's go.'

—

Their pace was slower now, but stealth was more important than speed. Atius and Silus were both proficient in disguising their tracks, but Silus was impressed that Odo also took care not to disturb the leaf litter, to break branches or leave any of the other tell-tale signs that might show a tracker their passage.

Atius was able to sustain the brisk walking pace, and as day dawned, the risk of tripping on concealed roots and rocks receded. Silus tried to draw Atius into conversation, but whenever he tried to bring the subject round to Atius' mission, how he had been captured, Atius would just glance at Odo and squeeze his mouth shut. Eventually Silus gave up trying, and they walked on in silence as Silus tried to adjust to this new uncharacteristically taciturn side of his friend.

Their rest breaks were short, and though each time Odo, who showed not the slightest sign of fatigue, scouted ahead, Atius was still reluctant to talk about their journey and capture. But when the scout wasn't around, he asked after Tituria, how was Lipari, even how Issa was faring in her old age. As soon as Odo returned, though, he clammed up again.

The terrain varied between forest, hill, marsh and farmland. Atius noted that their progress was much quicker than on his outward journey, without the terrible winter conditions they had had to cope with. Although there was enough rain and mud to make sure they weren't enjoying themselves, by the time night fell they had covered a considerable distance, and had been travelling west for some time.

When they stopped for some rest and sleep in the lee of a rocky cliff face, with dusk approaching, Silus and Odo left Atius, and scrambled to the top of the cliff to survey their position. Silus looked out over the countryside, green rolling hills dotted with the white blobs of distant sheep. The setting sun illuminated the underside of the clouds, turning them into upside-down red-orange hillocks. Silus was held by the beauty for a moment.

Odo interrupted his reverie.

'Your friend doesn't like me.'

'Don't take it personally. He has been held captive and badly treated by Germans for weeks.'

'Chatti. Not Alamanni.'

'It's hard for us to tell the difference sometimes.'

'Are you talking about our appearance or our sense of honour?'

Silus shook his head, but before he could think of a reply, Odo tapped his arm and pointed.

'Over there. Movement.'

Silus followed the direction of his outstretched finger and squinted. Then he saw it, cresting some distant hills, a small group of figures. They were too indistinct for him to make out any details.

'What can you see?' he asked.

'A dozen Chatti. Carrying spears. On foot, no horses, no dogs.'

'Do you think they can see us?'

'I'm not sure.'

'Come on, let's get out of their sight, and let's get moving. No time for rest after all.'

They hurried down the scree of the steep slope bordering the rock cliff face and found Atius fast asleep. Silus shook him gently and he woke with a yelp, wide eyes looking around him wildly, panting, before he focused on Silus' face and he swallowed and regained control.

'We've got company. Two or three miles back, but they must have picked up a trail. We need to get going again.'

Atius grimaced, but got to his feet. 'I feel completely refreshed,' he said sardonically. 'Come on.'

Odo led them on an unpredictable route at a brisk pace. Atius made no word of complaint, but Silus could see the tension in the lines of his face as he fought exhaustion.

Silus wondered how long he could continue. Would they reach safety before Atius gave out completely?

Night descended fully, but as they were no longer travelling under the impenetrable canopies of the trees, and there was intermittent moonlight peeking out between gaps in the clouds, they could move more freely than before. They took short breaks for Atius' sake, though Silus wasn't complaining about them either. His feet were sore and his calves and shins ached from the constant up and down of the paths through the hills.

When dawn broke, Silus was pleased with how much ground they had covered, and they hadn't noticed any indication of pursuit.

'How far from the border now, do you think?' he asked Odo.

'Two days' walk, I would say. But less than that until we are out of Chatti territory.'

'Will they give up the chase when we leave Chatti lands?'

'I'm not sure.'

Silus thought about it. Atius was getting slower. They had foraged plenty of food and water on the way, but Atius' body had taken too much punishment for him to keep up the pace much longer. If they carried on like this, Silus was worried he would end up having to carry him.

'We go straight,' he said. 'No more deviations. We have to hope that we have lost them. Steady pace, not too fast. We'll try to get out of reach of the Chatti by nightfall.'

Odo nodded agreement.

'Sounds good,' said Atius. 'I'm looking forward to a bath and a drink.'

Silus smiled. That was a bit more like his old friend.

Odo led the way as usual. Silus matched pace with Atius, and tried to take his mind off the ever-present pain from aching muscles and joints with light conversation and reminiscences.

'Remember that girl in Numidia? The one with the missing front teeth? What did you see in her?'

Atius grinned and Silus' spirit lifted at the sight.

'It wasn't what you could see. It was what she could do when the lamps were out. Let me tell you, that gap in her teeth meant she could do more than just whistle.'

Silus laughed. 'Well, think of all the girls waiting for you in Colonia.'

Atius' grin disappeared.

'I'm sort of off girls, I think.'

Silus looked at him in surprise. Then he thought of the little priestess, and he wondered again what Atius had suffered. He suspected the torture had been more mental in Atius' case, compared to the very obvious and horrific physical torments that Eustachys had been exposed to. What a wreck the priestess had made of that man. Eustachys had known what he was doing. He had no desire to live any further.

The countryside became more populous as they progressed westwards, and they frequently had to circumnavigate farms and small settlements. They kept off the main roads as best they could, and used animal tracks and shepherds' paths as often as possible to make their way easier. Silus was pleased with how much ground they had covered by the time the sun was past its zenith and beginning its descent.

But as they emerged from a small woodland that afternoon, Odo suddenly stopped and held up his hand. Silus and Atius froze, trying to work out what he had seen.

Silus scanned around, then saw it. Movement, behind them and to their left. Nearer than before, maybe just a mile. A small group of warriors, descending a grassy hill.

Should they scurry back into cover? Drop to the ground? Stay still?

The choice became irrelevant when a shout went up from the warriors. Although it was attenuated by distance and wind, it was clearly a shout of recognition and alert.

'They've seen us,' said Odo. 'They are pointing our way.'

'Shit,' said Silus. 'Shit, shit, shit.'

They were so close. Refuge was surely not much more than a day away. But it might as well have been in India. There was no way they could reach it, no possibility of outrunning their pursuers with Atius in his current condition. They had no horses. Silus had considered stealing some, but they would have been useless over much of the terrain they'd had to traverse. They couldn't hide. The woodland they had just emerged from was too small – the warriors would search it and find them swiftly.

He looked at Atius, despairingly.

'Leave me,' said Atius.

'What are you talking about?'

'You have a chance of outrunning them without me. With me, you have no chance. Go. There is no time for discussion.'

Silus looked at him in incomprehension.

'Have you gone mad?'

'Leave me the spear. I'll slow them down. But I won't let them take me alive. Not again.'

Silus slapped him, open-handed but forceful, leaving a red mark on Atius' cheek. Atius put his hand to his face in open-mouthed shock.

'I left retirement for you. I left Tituria behind. I sailed across the sea, rode over land to Germania, tracked you through barbarian lands, was captured. For you! Do you think I would leave you behind now?'

Atius shook his head. 'You're so fucking stupid, Silus.'

'That has been pointed out before.'

Atius grinned. 'Fine, let's see how far we get. And when they catch us, we fight. But I mean it, Silus. I won't be taken prisoner. And I suggest you don't let them take you either.'

'We'll cross that bridge when we reach it.'

Silus turned to Odo. The young lad was looking anxiously at the warriors, who were already closing the gap as they hurried towards him.

'Boy, you have done your job well. You have upheld your oath. You rescued us. Now I release you. You don't have to die with us. Flee, get to safety. Go and tell Oclatinius what happened here.'

Odo looked grave. He held out his hand, and Silus shook it.

'You're a good man, Silus,' he said. Then he turned and ran. Silus and Atius watched him go for a moment, haring at speed across the landscape.

'Come on,' Silus said to Atius, and they started off at a pace that was half walk, half jog.

Silus wondered if they should save some energy for the inevitable fight when the Chatti warriors caught them, then decided it really didn't matter either way. A sense of inevitability had come over him, and with it, a sense of peace. If he had to die, doing so in combat, with his friend by his side, was not the worst way. Dying in captivity, tortured by barbarians bent on vengeance. That was a bad death. He considered the spear in his hand, whether he would be able to turn it on himself somehow when the time came. He supposed he would use it on Atius first, then brace it on the ground and fall on it, like Romans traditionally did with their swords, although its length would be problematic. Another bridge to cross when he came to it.

'He showed his true colours in the end,' said Atius between deep breaths.

'Odo? What makes you say that?'

'No sense of loyalty, like all these Germans.'

'Why do you hate him so much? Is it because of what you have been through?'

'Look, Silus. We had a guide, too. A Bructeri called Aldric. He was working for the Chatti the whole time, leaving them signs so they could track us. It's his fault my men are dead. His fault I was captured. That Eustachys...' He broke off abruptly.

'Odo isn't like that. He is Alamanni, not Bructeri or Chatti, for a start.'

'They are all the same.'

'And he has proven himself, again and again.'

'It's just a ploy. Getting you into his confidence.'

'For what purpose? It doesn't make any sense. Look, Silus, I like him. He even invited me into his house.'

'He did what?'

'It was on the way. We stayed for the night.'

'Don't tell me, he ended up in your bed.'

'Fuck you, Atius!'

They continued on in angry silence for a while. Then Silus said, 'It wasn't him that ended up in my bed.'

'What? Who?'

'Well. I thought it was a slave girl who came to my room in the night. I only found out when it was too late that it was his sister.'

Atius turned to stare at him, then burst out laughing.

'Christos, Silus.'

'Don't tell, for Mithras' sake.'

Atius glanced back over his shoulder. 'I don't think I will get the chance.'

Silus looked back too. The pursuing warriors were gaining on them, there was no doubt. Maybe half a mile back now. He could make out their numbers, if not their arms and features at this distance. They came on at a slow jog, and Silus felt like a stag being worn down by a wolf pack, harrying and harassing until the prey dropped from exhaustion and was torn apart.

They stopped speaking for a while, saving their breath. But as the inevitable got closer, as Silus felt his lifespan measured in paces, in pounding heartbeats rather than in days or even hours, he felt curiosity getting the better of him.

'What was all this about, Atius? Why the fuck were you out here?'

Atius looked behind him again. 'They're close.'

Silus looked back too. The gap was down to a quarter of a mile, and closing rapidly as Atius slowed. They were hurrying along a well-used cart track now, no longer needing to worry about concealment. Ahead and to the right was a small copse. Silus indicated it, and they headed towards the trees. Maybe it would make no difference, but a bit of cover might make the fight easier. Though he knew it would make no difference in the end, the urge to survive was strong.

'Tell me,' said Silus.

'Really? Now?'

'If not now, when?'

'It doesn't matter any more.'

'Yes it fucking matters. We are both throwing our lives away, for the sake of this mission. So what the fuck was it?'

Silus could hear the shouts clearly now. The copse was a hundred yards away, but the warriors only fifty yards behind. Atius was breathing hard, and his pace could not even be considered a fast walk any more. They weren't going to make it.

'Atius! Why are we about to die?' he yelled in exasperation.

'I'm not telling you, alright? You don't want to know. Die happy, in ignorance and honour.'

'Romans. Stop!' The shouted order came from right behind them. Silus grabbed Atius' arm, pulling him to a halt, and they turned to face their attackers. Silus held the spear before them, just like the Chatti boy he had taken it from had. He felt about as dangerous as that child, before the angry, leering Chatti. They formed a semi-circle around the two Romans, keeping just out of reach. Silus recognised the leader. It was Radulf, the head of the party that had previously captured Odo and him. He spoke to the warrior next to him, who could obviously speak some Latin and could translate.

'Throw your spear down, Roman,' said the translator.

'Come and take it,' retorted Silus.

The Chatti leader laughed and spat some coarse Germanic words. 'Do you think it would be difficult?' came the translation.

'You might be surprised.'

Radulf motioned two of his men forward. Silus gripped the spear tight, uncertain whether to lunge, stand his ground, or turn it on Atius. Atius stood to his side, defiant, but weak and unarmed. The two muscular warriors approaching both held axes. Silus had the reach over them, but it wouldn't hold them at bay for long. They moved apart so Silus could not keep the spear trained on them both at once. Slowly they advanced.

And then stopped.

Silus feinted at them, wondering if he really looked that menacing. The warriors stepped backwards.

'Ha. You see what it's like to face a Roman man to man, don't you?' He was half-aware that he was babbling, maybe losing control, but he didn't care. He took a step forward. 'Come on then, you fuckers. I'm here, come and take me if you dare.'

The warriors took another step back and Silus laughed, shaking the spear one-handed in their direction. 'Cowards! Fight me!'

He felt Atius' light touch on his arm.

'Silus.'

'Is this what the Chatti are made of?' taunted Silus. 'No braver than old women?'

'Silus,' said Atius again. Silus glanced sideways at him, and Atius nodded backwards. Keeping half an eye on the Chatti, Silus turned.

Arrayed in two ranks, with bows strung and arrows nocked, were two dozen mounted Germanic warriors. In the centre, on a bay stallion, sat Odo's father, Boda. Next to him, seated on a grey, shaggy-maned pony, was Odo. Silus stared at him in disbelief, and Odo gave him a cheeky grin.

Radulf took one step forward. He was big, as leaders in German tribes often were, Silus had noted, and he carried his war-axe across chest in two hands. He called out a challenge to the horsemen in Germanic dialect. Boda replied in Latin, Silus presumed for the benefit of himself and Atius.

'I am Boda of the Alamanni. You are trespassing in Alamanni lands, Chatti.'

'This is Radulf of the Chatti,' called out the Chatti translator. 'He demands that you let him take these criminals.'

'What is their crime?'

'Murder. Spying. Sacrilege.'

'We have a witness who says that is not true.'

Radulf scanned the lines of the horsemen, and his eyes came to rest on Odo. He pointed, his finger shaking, and yelled at him in German. Odo replied defiantly in the same language.

Boda replied in a steady voice that was full of threat.

'Tell Radulf that he had better beware whom he calls traitor. Odo is my son.'

Radulf glared at Ansigar and spoke directly to him, his tone loud and furious.

Boda replied in Latin. 'You are in no position to make threats, Chatti. Now leave our lands immediately, or we will fill you all full of arrows.'

The Alamanni raised their bows now, aimed and pulled the strings taut to their ears. Silus could see the tension in their arms, the quivering muscles. They could only hold that position for so long before they had to loose, or let the string go slack. Radulf glared at Boda, and they held each other's stare. But Boda, from his elevated position on horseback, with superior numbers and an advantage in ranged weaponry, remained confident and imperturbable. So it was Radulf who broke the eye contact first, looking away with a curse and motioning his men to back off. Boda gave a signal to his archers and they eased the strain off their bowstrings and pointed the bows downwards.

Radulf shouted what Silus presumed were more threats and curses at Ansigar, then turned and stalked away, his men following reluctantly behind.

Silus watched them go, releasing a breath he didn't know he had been holding. Beside him, Atius' legs buckled and he sank to the ground.

Odo dismounted and ran over to them both.

'Is he hurt?' asked their young guide, voice full of concern.

'Just exhausted,' said Silus.

Atius looked up. 'I thought you had left us.'

Odo looked offended. 'Haven't I proven myself to you by now?'

When it became obvious that Atius wasn't going to reply, Silus filled in. 'Of course you have. More than once.' Silus gave Atius an annoyed glance, but Atius was staring at his feet, withdrawn. He turned to Odo.

'You ran for help?'

Odo nodded. 'We're in Alammani territory now. I knew we were near my uncle's village. When I asked him for help, he gathered his men and rode straight here.'

Boda had been watching Radulf and his men retreating, and when he was satisfied, he dismounted and approached Silus.

'You brought my son home.'

'It kind of feels like it's the other way round,' said Silus.

'That isn't how he tells it. He thinks you are a man of courage and honour.' He looked at Atius. 'This is the friend that you came to Germania to rescue?'

Odo had obviously told his father more than he should have, but Silus could hardly hold that against him in the circumstances. He nodded. 'Yes, this is Atius.'

'You journeyed far and risked everything for him. Every man should have a friend such as you.'

Silus had the grace to look humble.

'We are only a few miles from my house. You and your friend can ride with us, and then you can rest and eat.'

Silus smiled, and then it suddenly hit him. He had done it. He had got Atius out, and they had both escaped with their lives.

He put a hand down to help Atius to his feet.

'We're safe, Atius.'

Atius looked around at the Alamanni warriors, expression unreadable.

'No one is ever truly safe,' he said.

–

Boda told tall tales about great hunts from his youth as he became drunker and drunker on the strong beer. Stories of facing down charging boars with only a spear, of tracking a lone wolf that had been stealing lambs for days through winter snow before taking it down with a single arrow. Odo drank and ate sparingly, and listened to his father with evident equal parts amusement and admiration. Ada made sure the slaves were attentive in keeping them all supplied with meat and drink, and otherwise kept a benign eye on the feast, smiling indulgently, but clearly lovingly, at Boda.

Silus had found himself sitting next to Ima, though he wasn't quite sure how that had happened. When it was Silus' turn to tell stories, and he told them of Rome and Syracuse and Alexandria, he could see her from the corner of his eye, hanging on his every word. He found himself blushing and tripping over his words because of the close attention, but no one else seemed to notice.

Least of all Atius, who was quiet and sullen throughout the evening. When he got up to relieve himself, Silus followed him outside. He caught up with Atius standing against a tree.

'What the fuck is wrong with you?'

'Can't a man have a piss in peace?'

'Why are you behaving like this?'

Atius let out a sigh, and the smell of urine filled the air. 'Behaving like what, Silus?'

'Like an ungrateful, ungracious ass.'

Atius finished, shook, and put himself away. He turned to Silus.

'What should I be grateful for exactly, Silus? For being captured, for being tortured for weeks on end. For seeing my men slaughtered, the man I was supposed to protect lose his mind from the torments he was put through?'

'That was the Chatti. Not the Alamanni.'

'They are all the same. All Germans, all barbarians.'

'You know that's not true. Look at the way the Alammani live. They are almost Romans. They seem to want to be part of the Empire.'

'You can put a toga on a pig, doesn't make it a senator.'

'You're being ridiculous. And unreasonable. I know you have been through a lot...'

'You know nothing.'

'Fine, fine. I don't know how bad it was. But I do know you would still be there if it wasn't for Odo.'

'Your pet guide. Whose sister you fucked?'

'Keep your voice down,' hissed Silus.

'How do you think he will feel if he finds out? Think he will still be your special friend? Or will he turn on you, like my guide turned on me.'

'Odo has been nothing but loyal. I owe him my life. And so do you.'

Atius turned to Silus and stood for a moment, face to face with him.

'I'm going to find a barn to sleep in. Somewhere where I can only smell animals, and not Germans.'

Silus watched him go, bewildered and exasperated.

When he went back inside, Boda was singing and Ewald, Odo's younger brother, was accompanying him on a hand-held drum. Silus took his seat next to Ima. While all eyes were on the performing pair, she put her hand on the inside of his thigh and squeezed.

He knew then that she was going to come to him again that night. And he knew, too, that he wasn't going to refuse.

Chapter Twelve

Their arrival back in Colonia felt flat and anti-climactic to Silus. The sky was grey, with a fine, persistent drizzle hanging in the air. No cheering crowds. No legionaries lining the streets, saluting them as they passed.

A donkey cart, travelling too fast, swerved to miss a sedan chair and drove through a puddle, splashing Silus with cold, muddy water. He shouted a curse at the cart driver, who made an obscene gesture back as he disappeared down the street. Silus looked down at himself, tunic brown and soaking. He wiped his face, and noticed Atius smiling. Not guffawing with laughter, as the man of old would have done, but it was better than nothing.

Silus wanted to get Atius to a tavern and find him a bed. The day's journey had left him looking fragile once more. But Atius insisted on reporting back to Festus and Oclatinius immediately, and his almost frantic expression caused Silus to relent. Silus insisted that they approach Oclatinius first. He had no trust in Festus, and much as he resented Oclatinius' manipulations and threats, he still respected him and believed in his loyalty. He sent Odo off to procure them rooms, and he and Atius went in search of their commanding officer.

After a few enquiries, they tracked him down to a room in the governor's residence, which building Caracalla had made his headquarters for the campaign.

A civilian slave announced them and they were shown into a spacious study, with a large desk and two chairs. As it turned out, Festus was with Oclatinius anyway, and the Commander of the Sacred Bedchamber and the Head of the Arcani both got to their feet and stared as the two men entered.

Festus wore an expression of shock, and it was Oclatinius who recovered his composure first.

'You could have made yourself a little less slovenly before presenting yourself, the pair of you,' he said.

This was the point where Atius usually said something recklessly smart and funny. But now he said nothing. Silus gave him a sideways glance, then replied.

'Sorry, sir. Atius didn't want to delay his report.'

'You're alive,' said Festus, finally finding his voice, though it barely reached above a whisper. 'But... how?'

'Would you like our full account now, sir?' asked Silus.

'No, no, it can wait. Just tell me, Atius. Eustachys?'

Atius shook his head.

Festus pursed his lips. His mouth formed words as if he had momentarily forgotten how to express himself. Eventually he said, 'And did he...?'

'He did not reveal what he knew to the barbarians. You trained him well.'

Festus nodded, then another thought seemed to occur to him.

'And did he tell you?'

'He did.'

Festus whitened. 'And you kept it secret too?'

'Yes. I didn't even tell Silus here.'

Silus gritted his teeth, frustrated, feeling like a child eavesdropping on a conversation the adults didn't want him hearing, and talking in code. 'Yes, the sparrow is D-E-A-D but don't tell you-know-who until we have found one that looks the same.'

'I didn't train you,' said Festus. 'How did you hold out?'

'I was lucky. They didn't give me quite the same attention they lavished on Eustachys. If they had, I doubt I would have lasted the day before I told them everything.'

Festus looked over at Oclatinius, whose expression was grim. 'Tell Festus everything,' said Oclatinius. 'Then go and get some rest. Silus, walk with me.'

Oclatinius put his arm around Silus' shoulder and ushered him out of the room, shutting the door behind them. Silus turned to see Atius slump into a chair, before he disappeared from view.

'What's going on?' said Silus angrily. 'Atius won't talk to me. He's behaving like someone completely different. I don't know him any more. And there is some shady shit about his mission, and I want to know what it is.'

Oclatinius sighed, and guided him down the corridor, away from the room where Festus and Atius were talking in private. 'Actually, you really don't want to know.'

'That's what Atius told me. Which makes me want to know all the more.'

'It will all become apparent, all too soon.' He ushered Silus to a side door, and the duty Praetorian guards came to attention at the sight of Oclatinius. 'Go and eat and drink, then meet me back here in an hour. Caracalla will want to see you. He has a task.'

'Of course he fucking does.'

Silus stomped off in search of a tavern.

—

'There is someone I need you to kill.'

Caracalla had wasted little time on pleasantries. Silus thought his mood seemed dark. He was perpetually frowning, but the lines on his forehead seemed deeper than Silus remembered, and he often pressed his fingers to his temples on both sides, like he was trying to relieve the pain of a throbbing headache. Silus guessed that was what happened to you when you killed your brother while he was in his mother's arms. When a man's character became darker, it had implications for all those around him. When that man was Emperor, what implications did it have for the Empire, for the world?

Oclatinius, who stood before the emperor at Silus' side, seemed unperturbed. To the right of the throne sat Macrinus, dark hair cropped short in contrast to a long curly beard which was streaked with white. Silus knew Caracalla had made him Praetorian prefect after Sextus Varius Marcellus was sent to Numidia as governor, but as he had not been back to Rome since he had left with Marcellus, he had had nothing to do with Macrinus since his promotion. Silus sized him up, coming quickly to the hasty conclusion that he was no Marcellus. Was it something in his eyes that made him seem untrustworthy, or was he just jumping to unfounded conclusions?

'Yes, Augustus. Who would you have me kill?'

'His name is Suabgast. He is the leader of one of the Alamanni factions.'

'It will be done, Augustus. Would it be helpful for me to know why?'

Caracalla exchanged a glance with Macrinus, who narrowed his eyes fractionally.

'There is a delegation of Alamanni leaders currently in this city. They are here to discuss an alliance between their people and Rome.'

'That is great news, Augustus,' said Silus. 'My experience of the Alamanni people has been very positive. The Alamanni are much closer to Rome than most barbarians, and I'm sure want nothing more than peace. My guide, Odo, was...'

Caracalla waved him into a silence. 'That's all very well, but it is clear from Festus' spies that this Suabgast is secretly opposed to peace, and will do anything to prevent it. You are to kill him, discreetly. It must look like an accident. And you are to tell no one outside this room. Is that clear?'

'Perfectly, Augustus.'

'Be careful. He is a strong fighter, a skilled military tactician and a persuasive, charismatic leader. Do not give him any chances. Do this well for me, Silus, and I might consider recalling your young friend back from Lipari.'

'You will?' Silus couldn't hide his surprise. 'You are most generous and merciful, Augustus.'

'Yes, yes. You are dismissed. Oclatinius, take him away and tell him how to find Suabgast.'

Silus bowed and retreated, a thrill of hope and excitement growing inside him.

—

The Alamanni delegation were housed in a large domus on the outskirts of Colonia, one of several properties owned by the Emperor in the city. Oclatinius had told Silus that Festus' spies had reported on Suabgast's movements. He was said to hate the city, preferring the forests and open fields, and felt hemmed in, penned in the domus all day. Since his own guards would not permit him to walk the streets alone, he had taken to visiting the roof of the domus after dinner, where he could look out over an open expanse, albeit of stone and timber, not living trees, and he could breathe the clear air, high above the stench of the city streets.

It simplified things greatly for Silus. Killing someone and escaping without being caught was never straightforward. Making it look like an accident was fraught with problems. Shoving someone under the wheels of a heavy cart on a busy street ran a high risk of witnesses. Setting things up to look like a random mugging ran the risk of raising suspicions, and there were often bodyguards to overcome in that situation. Dropping some masonry on the victim's head from high up as they passed could work, but it meant knowing their precise movements in advance, and besides, it was incredibly hard to aim a roof tile or brick with any precision from three storeys up. It often came down to attempting to administer a poison that made a death look like it was from natural causes, but getting the victim to consume the substance voluntarily in a sufficient quantity meant hiding it in food, and then the poison had to act slowly enough that it wasn't obvious the food had been tampered with, but quickly enough that he did actually die in a reasonable timeframe.

Falls, on the other hand, were commonplace. Anyone walking on a rooftop took a risk, what with the poor construction and crumbling stonework of many buildings. So Silus waited until dusk, and them clambered up a side wall that was mainly in shadow. It wasn't a trivial climb, but there were sufficient handholds where bricks had come loose or cement had cracked that he made it to the top with only one heart-stopping moment, when his foot had slipped and he had dangled from the fingertips of both hands before his feet found their grip once more.

Once he was on the roof, he settled down behind a marble pot in which narcissi were growing, their buds forming, ready to flower. The rooftop was flat, designed to offer a garden space to the occupants, as an alternative to the enclosed peristylium which Silus could see at the far side. This building was not the tallest in Colonia Agrippinensis. Some distance away were a few large insulae, nowhere near as numerous as in Rome, but plentiful enough to house some of the urban poor. Nevertheless, the view was clear enough that Silus could see why a man used to the countryside would want to come up here. He settled himself comfortably, watched the top of the stairs, where they led up from the peristylium, and waited.

Silus heard the footsteps before he saw his prey. Though the sun was below the horizon, there was still enough of a glow in the sky to illuminate Suabgast clearly as his head appeared at the top of the steps. Though his hair was long, he was balding on top, and he was older than Silus had expected. But like all the Germanic leaders, he was bulky, and he carried himself with an air of assurance. Silus watched him, staying motionless, his breathing steady and even, mouth open so his broken nose didn't whistle.

Suabgast stretched his arms out wide and took a deep breath, his barrel chest expanding. He looked around him, and Silus ducked down as the German's gaze drifted in his direction. After a moment he peeked over the edge of the pot again. Suabgast strolled towards the edge of the rooftop to look out across the streets. His attention was caught by a scuffle in the street, two soldiers drunkenly and ineffectually wrestling and throwing punches.

Silus drew his knife from his belt. He hoped not to use it, but he realised he might need it if his victim put up a fight. He came closer, footsteps silent. One push was all it would take. Simple.

'You are here to kill me?'

Suabgast hadn't moved, his back still firmly to Silus. How had he known he was there? These Germans had sharp senses. Silus halted, not sure whether to reply. Suabgast slowly turned. His gaze dropped to Silus' knife, and he nodded as if confirming it to himself.

'May I ask why?' His voice seemed full of sadness. Silus knew he shouldn't engage in conversation with the person he was about to kill. It only ever made him feel more guilty later. But somehow he felt he owed this stranger an explanation.

'You are going to ruin the peace talks.'

'Am I really?'

'Peace between the Alamanni and Rome is such a precious and fragile thing. I have Alamanni friends. I don't want to be on the opposite side of a war with their people.'

'And you think I am an impediment to this?'

'So I have been informed.'

'I am thinking it would be useless to try to change your mind.'

'Even if you did, I would still have a job to do.'

'And I will try to stop you. But if I am unsuccessful, I want you to know that I desire peace for my people more than life itself. I do not trust that Rome feels the same, whatever words come from your Emperor's mouth tomorrow.'

There was nothing more to say. Silus took two slow, cautious steps forward, his knife held in a firm grip by his side, watching for any sudden movements. Even so, when Suabgast pounced, Silus was nearly taken by surprise. He was quick for a big man, and he lunged forward for Silus' knife hand. Silus jerked it away, twisted, and then found himself in a grapple. Suabgast hugged him with both arms, and squeezed hard. The pressure built on Silus' chest, until he couldn't get a breath.

He thought about bringing the knife round and plunging it into Suabgast's back. But he wasn't sure he could get the angle to deliver a blow with any power, and besides, stab wounds would not make it look like an accident. Instead, he pushed himself backwards, and as Suabgast tottered forward, he twisted and stuck a straight leg out. Suabgast tripped, teetered, then fell heavily. When he hit the ground, his head slammed backwards into the tiles and his grip broke. Silus twisted free and took two deep breaths.

Suabgast was slow to recover. He rolled onto his hands and knees, but by the time he had got back to his feet, Silus was behind him, with the knife against his throat.

'Walk forward,' said Silus. Suabgast did as he was told, until he was at the edge of the rooftop once more. He paused there, looking up at the sky rather than down at the drop. Silus prepared to shove him in the back.

'Let me take this step myself,' said Suabgast. Silus hesitated, then took the knife away. He kicked some masonry off the edge of the rooftop, making it look like part had crumbled.

'Go to your gods,' said Silus, 'and ask them for peace.'

Suabgast stepped out. He made no sound as he plummeted downwards, until the thud of his impact on the cobbles below. Silus looked down. Suabgast lay still, limbs askew.

The two soldiers who had been fighting earlier and were now drinking together rushed over to him, checking him for signs of life. Silus ducked back into cover before

233

they could look up and see him. He looked around him, making sure there were no signs of disturbance. He righted a small marble statue that had toppled over but fortunately not smashed. Then, with one last glance towards the spot from where Suabgast had fallen, he scurried back to the far side of the roof, and scuttled back down the wall. Once on the street, he made sure no one had seen his descent, and then took a slow and casual walk back to his quarters.

Chapter Thirteen

Silus waved as he caught Odo's eye on the far side of the pavilion. Odo smiled and waved back. Beside him Oclatinius exchanged a look with Atius that Silus couldn't read, and he felt an unease for which he couldn't quite pinpoint the source.

'What?' he asked.

'What?' replied Atius.

Silus turned back to Odo. He was seated on a bench next to his father Boda, about halfway back in the audience. Not the most important of the Alamanni, not the least. Odo nudged his father and pointed to Silus, and Boda lifted his hand in a salute which Silus returned. Seeing them together gave Silus a pang of guilt. He was sure they wouldn't approve, if they knew about him and Ima. But he had nothing to really be sorry for. Ima had seduced him, after all. Twice. And though he still thought about his wife every day, she had been dead a long time now.

Still, there was a nagging feeling that he had somehow let Odo down, and for reasons that weren't clear to him, the boy's approval felt important.

The general chatter died down as Caracalla entered the pavilion, followed by Julia Domna and Macrinus and four of his German bodyguard. The Germans chosen over the usual Praetorians at important conferences to impress the gathered Alamanni, no doubt. Politics over ceremony.

Caracalla walked to the raised seat that had been prepared for him, but remained standing. He waited until Domna and Macrinus were seated, then spoke.

'My friends of the Alemmani confederation, greetings. To all you chiefs and leaders and noble warriors, I bid you welcome to the part of Germania that belongs to Rome.'

There was a smattering of polite applause. Silus thought he detected an air of caution amongst the Alamanni, willing to hear what Caracalla had to say, but reserving judgement on whether to accept it or not.

'Rome and the tribes of Germania have a long history of warfare and strife,' continued Caracalla. 'Since the Teutones and Cimbri first clashed with the Roman Republic, and were defeated by Gaius Marius, through the time of your famous victory under Arminius against Varus in the Teutoburg forest, to a time within living memory when the Marcomanni fought our great Emperor Marcus Aurelius, Rome and Germania have struggled along our mutual border.

'This has brought great suffering and destruction. Armies on both sides have been massacred and enslaved. It drains our resources when we both have problems elsewhere.

'I have recently defeated the tribes of Caledonia, in a tremendous victory for which I was awarded the title Britannicus Maximus. And soon I must march to the opposite end of the empire, to deal with the troublesome Parthians. It would help Rome and myself greatly to know there was a settled border along the Rhenus.

'For your part, I know you want no war with Rome. Yet not all the tribes of Germania feel the same. The

236

Chatti and the tribes at the mouth of the Albis river plot against us, and against you. They resent your romanisation, your closeness to the Empire, and they wish to crush you just as much as they wish to drive us from our territories in Germania, maybe all the way back to Rome.'

There was a general murmur of agreement among the Alemmani leaders, though a minority shook their heads and muttered angrily.

'Noble chiefs, the Chatti and their allies are our common enemy. I propose today an alliance between the Alamanni confederacy, and their true friend, myself, Imperator Caesar Marcus Aurelius Severus Antoninus Pius Augustus Britannicus Maximus, on behalf of the senate and people of Rome.'

This now brought cheers of approval from the majority of the audience, though some remained sullen and silent.

'Together, we shall join forces, and crush the Chatti. I will then depart for my war in the east, and the Alamanni will rule Germania Magna as the unrivalled power in the region. What say you?'

There was a long pause, then a grey-haired, stooped man who had been seated on the front row got slowly to his feet. Though he obviously spoke Latin well, with only a light Germanic accent, his voice was hesitant and slow.

'Augustus, I thank you on behalf of the Alamanni confederation for inviting us here today. I am Chnodomar, son of Serapio, son of Chnodomar. The chiefs and princes of the tribes of the Alamanni elected myself and Suabgast as joint Paramount Kings of the confederacy. After Suabgast's unfortunate accident yesterday, I find myself in the troubling situation of having to speak for the whole of the Alamanni alone.'

At the mention of Suabgast's name, Silus' heart suddenly started pounding, and he felt a drop of sweat trickling down the back of his neck. The thought that anyone would notice his discomfort made him sweat even more, not helped by some angry, disbelieving mutters at the mention of an accident. Still, they remained in the minority. Obviously enough believed that Suabgast's death had not been deliberate to keep the peace talks on track, and that was what mattered. And no one seemed to have noticed Silus' sudden outbreak of perspiration. Oclatinius put a calming hand on his forearm. He took a deep breath, and his racing pulse began to slow.

'It is no secret that Suabgast had doubts about an alliance with Rome. His family suffered in the Marcomanni wars, and it was hard for him to adjust. My grandfather too fought against your Emperor Marcus Aurelius. But I was taught at his knee that the Romans are men of honour, men of their word, and though they may be fierce and ruthless in battle, their dignity and honesty is more important to them than their lives.

'I will do nothing without the agreement of the princes and chiefs with me today, but I tell you now that my desire is to accept your proposal for peace.' He turned to the seated conference delegates behind him. 'What say you? If you wish for peace, stand.'

For a moment, no one moved, an obvious reluctance to show the roll of the dice too soon. Then Odo stood, and yelled, 'I am for peace!'

Boda looked at his son with an expression equal parts exasperation and admiration. Then he stood as well, and with a hand on Odo's shoulder announced, 'I, too, am for peace.'

Their declarations broke the dam, and soon most of the chiefs, princes and minor nobles from all the tribes of the Alamanni were standing and declaring themselves for peace with Rome, amid cheers and clapping on their backs. A significant minority remained seated, glowering and cursing, but it was clear what the majority decision was.

Chnodomar turned back to Caracalla.

'On behalf of all the people of the Alamanni, I accept your offer of an alliance.'

'I ask you then,' said Caracalla, 'to summon your warriors. Bring them here, outside the walls of Colonia, ready for war, in seven days. That day, we will feast as brothers. And then, as one, we will march on the Chatti, and defeat them utterly.'

The Alamanni chiefs cheered and Chnodomar bowed his head. 'It shall be so.'

Caracalla smiled broadly, and for a brief moment, the deep lines in his forehead disappeared. He stepped forward and took Chnodomar's hand and pumped it enthusiastically. The meeting broke up as the delegates, at least those in favour of the outcome, mingled with the Romans and their German bodyguards. Those who didn't approve slunk quietly away.

Odo and Boda came over to Silus, who had been standing near the back of the pavilion next to the ever watchful Oclatinius.

'How does a lowly soldier like you get invited to an important peace conference like this?' said Boda.

Odo gave his father a backhand slap on the arm. 'He is not a lowly soldier. He is one of the Arcani, and you know it.'

Boda's grin showed that he did know it, and had been teasing Silus, although Silus himself wondered what made Oclatinius invite him along to these sort of events. Oclatinius had told him in the past that it was part of his ongoing education, to be familiar with the politics and strategies of the Empire, but Silus always felt out of place, that at any moment someone would turn to him and ask what he thought he was doing there. As Boda just had, albeit in jest.

'Oclatinius, this is my father Boda. Father, this is Oclatinius,' said Odo. 'He is the head of the Arcani.'

'The *secret* organisation, the Arcani, you mean,' admonished Oclatinius, though he was smiling. In truth, though the organisation of the Arcani kept a low profile, and its members tried to be discreet, most of the army and the politicians of Rome had heard of the Arcani, feared them, and only spoke of them in whispers, if at all. Which meant it could be very useful to announce that one was an Arcanus, from time to time. 'It is a pleasure to meet you, Boda. Silus has told me how brave and resourceful your son has been. I thought he would be. I have an eye for talent. Maybe one day, he will become an Arcanus himself.'

Odo blushed, his skin visibly reddening between the spots and the wispy tufts of his beard. 'And you know Atius,' he said, trying to cover up his embarrassment.

'Of course,' said Boda, and offered his hand. Atius hesitated, then shook it perfunctorily.

'Are you staying in Colonia?' asked Silus, throwing a glare at Atius.

'We will return home tomorrow,' said Boda, 'and gather our men for war. The planting is done, and if the gods will it, we will be home long before harvest.'

'Then tonight we will drink and gamble in the finest taverns in Colonia,' said Silus.

'I would love to join you,' said Oclatinius. 'But I have some reports to write, I am afraid.'

'Well, you will have to make do with the company of myself and Atius,' said Silus.

'I can't come either,' said Atius.

Silus looked at Atius. He had never known him to turn down a drink.

'Why not?'

'I'm not feeling well.'

Silus thought he should backtrack and tell Odo and his father that on reflection he too would be unavailable, so he could find out what was wrong with Atius, whether it was an ailment of his body or soul. But he felt a resentment towards his old friend. Ever since his rescue, he had been moody and withdrawn, and while it was understandable to some extent, Silus could not comprehend or countenance his rudeness towards Odo, who had been an essential part of the effort to rescue him and save his life.

'Fine, just me,' said Silus. 'But don't worry. I have a nose for trouble. By the end of the evening we will be bruised, drunk and broke.'

Boda laughed. 'That sounds like my type of celebration.'

'With your permission, Oclatinius, Boda, I will take my leave,' said Atius.

Silus watched him go, then shrugged his shoulders. He would come round in time. Tonight he was going to have fun. And try not to think about Ima, as he got drunk with her brother and father.

—

'You sent for us, sir.'

Oclatinius, seated at his desk, ignored Silus and Atius standing before him. He stared intently at the markings on a wax tablet before him. Silus tried to peek at the writing, but as far as he could see, it made no sense. Just random Latin words. Some kind of code, he guessed, from one element of Oclatinius' web of spies. He shuffled his feet impatiently.

Oclatinius looked up. 'Am I keeping you from something?' he asked testily.

'No, sir. Itchy foot.'

Oclatinius looked back down at the tablet, and Silus had the distinct impression he was no longer reading, just making Silus wait to annoy him. Eventually, he tossed the tablet aside.

'I've got a job for you both.'

It wasn't a shock; that was the usual reason for Oclatinius to summon them. But Silus wasn't in the mood for more killing. So it was a pleasant surprise when Oclatinius said, 'I need you to take a message to Mogontiacum.'

'A message. What sort of message?'

'A secret one.' He handed Silus a scroll, with a wax seal. 'Take this to the camp prefect in the Castra. You leave straight away.'

'But… the Alamanni warriors arrive the day after tomorrow. There is the feast and celebration of the new alliance.'

'Do I need to give you a reason why this message is urgent?' asked Oclatinius acidly.

'Well, it would be nice.' That was the sort of rejoinder Atius would have usually made, Silus realised. Atius just stood in silence, making no indication he was even listening.

'Just do as you are told, centurion.'

Silus took the scroll and saluted formally. 'Yes, sir. Right away, sir.'

'Get out.'

Silus strode out of Oclatinius' office, fuming.

'What are we, contractors for the cursus publicus now?' he said.

Atius shrugged. 'It's something to do, isn't it?'

Silus glared at him. 'What the fuck is wrong with you?' He sighed. 'Come on, let's go and find horses. It's well over a hundred miles. I guess we won't be going to the party.'

Silus took a glug from his cup of beer and looked across the table at Atius, who was toying listlessly with his food. They had covered good ground in the day and a half since they had left Colonia, riding at a steady pace, leaving them half a day from Mogontiacum. They'd stopped as night fell to change their horses at one of the stations of the cursus publicus, before finding a tavern. Silus tried again to make conversation, though he was on the verge of giving up and going to bed.

'Caracalla may bring Tituria back from exile,' he said.

'Oh,' said Atius. And then as an afterthought, 'That's good.'

'Is that all you have to say?'

Atius looked up from his plate, surprised.

'What?'

'I just told you that Tituria might be going back to Rome. The little girl who has been imprisoned on that forsaken island all this time. Whose family I killed, and which I feel guilty about every day. And all you say is, "that's good!"'

'What do you want me to say?'

'I don't know. Anything. Something to show me that you give a shit. Something to show me that the Atius who left Lipari to go back to work for the Arcani, who laughed and drank and fucked everything that moved, is still alive, and didn't fucking die in Germania.'

His voice had got louder and higher as he spoke, and he realised that his eyes had filled with tears, and they were overflowing down his cheeks. But he didn't care.

'You are my best friend. Close as a brother. I love you. But you are gone. I feel like I'm grieving for you, even when you are right in front of me.'

Atius' eyes were sorrowful. 'I'm sorry if I'm being distant. I've got a lot on my mind.'

'Then talk to me. You used to be able to tell me anything. Whether it was which girl you were chasing, or doubts about your faith.'

'I... I can't.'

'Is it what they did to you when you are in captivity? I get it. I get it was horrible. But you are tough, you can bounce back.'

'What do you know about it?'

'You think I haven't suffered? You forgot I watched my wife and daughter die?'

'No, but...' Atius sighed. 'I'm sorry. It's not that anyway.'

'What then?'

Atius took a deep drink. 'I suppose it doesn't matter any more. By the time we return, it will be all over.'

A chill settled over Silus. 'All over? What will be all over? What are you talking about?'

Atius pursed his lips.

'Don't hate me.'

Silus didn't move, didn't speak. His throat felt like it was threatening to close, to shut off his air supply. His eyes were locked on Atius' eyes, unwavering.

Atius swallowed. 'This mission is horseshit. Look at the message.'

Silus reached into his pack and drew out the scroll Oclatinius had handed him. He looked down at the wax seal doubtfully. The thought of opening it made him shiver, so ingrained was the prohibition against breaking an official seal. But Atius was scaring him. He broke the wax with his thumb and tore open the papyrus scroll. He read the message, then read it again. He turned the scroll over to check he hadn't missed something written on the other side. Then he read it one more time, to be sure.

'What the fuck is this?'

'What does it say?'

'It says, "Please thank the bearer of this message, and send him back to me. O."'

Atius nodded. 'I thought it would be something along those lines.'

'I don't understand.'

'Come on, Silus, you're not stupid.'

'He wanted us out of the way?'

'Not us. You. I'm just babysitting you.'

'What's going to happen?'

Atius put his palm over his lower face, covering his mouth.

'Come on,' said Silus impatiently. 'You've got this far.'

Atius took a deep breath, and told him. Silus stared as he spoke, disbelieving. When he had finished, Silus sat in stunned silence. When he could speak, his words were little more than a whisper.

'How long have you known?'

'Since before I was captured.'

Silus shook his head in disbelief.

'I can't let this happen.'

'It's too late. By the time you get there it will be all over.'

'I've got to try.'

'I can't let you.'

'You think you could stop me?' Silus' voice was a growl.

'Before... everything. Yes, I could have stopped you. Now?' He looked down at himself, a shadow of the powerful, muscular man he had once been. 'Probably not.'

'Then don't bother trying.' Silus stood abruptly, his stool tipping over backwards with a clatter. 'I'm going to see how fast these cursus publicus horses really are. As for you,' he pointed his finger, so the tip was only an inch from Atius' eye. His mouth worked as he tried out cutting phrases, and discarded them unspoken. 'Just stay away from me,' he said eventually.

Atius looked down into his beer, and did not look up again until Silus had strode out, slamming the door behind him.

—

He knew he would be too late, even as he rode at breakneck speed down the cobbled road. He stopped at every station of the cursus publicus along the way, leaping from the saddle of his sweating, breathless mount and shouting for a slave to bring him a fresh one, before galloping off into the night once more. There were few travellers on the road at night, the occasional farmer taking his vegetables to market, some richer merchants with tough, scarred veterans as bodyguards. Once, two bandits tried to stop him, standing in the middle of the road with swords drawn, signalling for him to halt. He rode them down, their screams as they writhed, clutching at broken limbs, fading into the distance.

But it wasn't enough. The sun rose, casting a beautiful fire across the underside of the low cloud in the east, and it continued higher as the mile markers to Colonia counted down with painful slowness. He had covered more miles faster than ever in his life. But the gathering was at noon. He wouldn't make it.

The sun must have been at its zenith when he reached the city gate. He raced through, yelling at the startled guards that he was on urgent business for the Emperor. The streets were emptier than usual, with conspicuously fewer soldiers marching and parading. Fewer citizens too. Many of them were former soldiers themselves, and had a nose for trouble, and had holed up with their families in their homes until whatever was about to happen had happened. He rode straight for the governor's villa, Caracalla's headquarters. The guards on duty were more diligent than those at the city gates and when he dismounted and tried to enter, they barred his way.

'Stand aside,' he said, breathless and weak-kneed.

'State your business,' said one of the guards, a Praetorian in immaculate uniform.

'I'm an Arcanus. Here to see the Emperor.'

He had no idea what he was going to say to Caracalla. He hoped inspiration would come. Maybe he would just get on his knees and beg. But the opportunity did not arise anyway.

'He's not here.'

The voice came from within the palace. He looked beyond the guards and saw Oclatinius walking towards him.

'You,' growled Silus. 'You knew about this. You sent me away because you knew I would try to stop it. In fact, I bet this was all your idea.'

Oclatinius shook his head sadly. 'No, this was all down to him. I can't take the credit. Or the blame.'

'Just tell me where.'

'You can't do anything.'

'I have to try.'

'Why?'

'Why? Because...' He wasn't sure he could put it into words. Maybe it was just because someone had to. And of course, there was Odo. 'Because it's wrong.'

'You think you know better than the Emperor what is right and wrong?'

'I know that for sure. Now tell me where it's happening, Oclatinius, or I swear to all the gods on Olympus I will never work for you for the rest of my life.'

Oclatinius shrugged. 'You will only be in time to be a witness.'

'If that's all I can be, I will be that.'

Oclatinius passed his hand over his eyes, and it suddenly struck Silus how old the spymaster was. He sighed.

'To the north-east of the city, about two miles out, there is a valley, with a small tributary of the Rhenus flowing through it. In the floodplain at the bottom, the warriors of the tribes of the Alamanni will be celebrating their new alliance with Rome.'

Silus opened his mouth, but he could not bring himself to thank him. Maybe Oclatinius wasn't responsible. But he had certainly done nothing to stop this. He turned on his heel, grabbed his horse's reins, remounted and kicked his heels into its flanks. The horse leapt into motion again, heading back for the city gates.

–

The gathered warriors of the Alamanni confederacy should have been an impressive sight. Tall, broad, fearsome looking. Not the sort of men you would want to be looking at from the pointed end of a sword. And present in vast numbers too. Seeing them all together in one place like this truly impressed on Silus how vast the Alamanni people were. And of course, many of the tribes remained at home, protecting their families from other tribes and predators, working the fields or making weapons and tools. On top of that, the Alamanni were just one of the many conglomerations of barbarians that inhabited Germania beyond the Empire's borders. United against Rome, they could be unstoppable.

But now they had come in peace. Unarmoured, unarmed, feasting, in friendship with their new allies. And noticeably drunk.

The smell of roasting meat hung over the gathering. The number of oxen and sheep slaughtered to feed this mass must have been vast. The Roman hosts seemed remarkably few in number, but they mingled with their guests, the slaves providing food and wine, and serving too as the object of various clumsy, unpleasant and unwanted attempts at seduction. A few Roman soldiers circulated as well, mainly centurions and officers, dressed in their uniforms, and armed. No doubt the Alamanni had been told their swords were purely for ceremonial purposes.

At the far end of the meeting place, opposite from where Silus had arrived, sat Caracalla, mounted on a pristine white gelding, flanked by mounted Praetorians. He was too far away for Silus to make out his features, but he could picture the creased forehead, frowning out at the revellers.

Silus tied his horse to a tree, and thrust his way into the throng of bodies. Despite what Oclatinius and Atius had said, despite his own misgivings, it looked like he really was in time. He would throw himself on Caracalla's mercy. Use reason, begging, threats, blackmail. Anything.

He pushed forward, thrusting bulky bodies aside, earning curses and shoves. Progress towards the Emperor was painfully slow.

'Clear the way,' he yelled. 'Stand aside.'

The Germans gave him curious stares. And suddenly he realised the Romans had gone. Not the slaves, of course, they still served, and were molested, oblivious. No one cared about them. But the Roman soldiers had slipped away, none to be seen. Silus, right in the centre of the mass of bodies, stood on his tiptoes, peering over the tall heads.

And then he saw them.

To the north, quietly, with perfect discipline, row upon row of legionaries had formed up on the slope of the hill, perpendicular to the river. He looked west and south and saw the same. The only place where no Roman soldiers stood was the riverbank, the fast-flowing water forming a natural barrier. He felt ice in his chest.

There was no stopping it now. All he could do was find Odo.

He grabbed the nearest German. 'Odo. Have you seen Odo? Boda, Ewald?' The barbarian looked at him with incomprehension, and replied in German. Frantic, Silus pushed through the crowd, craning his head this way and that.

'Odo,' he yelled. 'Odo!'

His shouting drew some attention, even over the singing and laughter of the feasting Alamanni. One tapped his shoulder and pointed. 'Odo.'

Silus saw his young friend, talking politely to a Roman slave girl, who was looking downwards demurely, maybe enjoying his company, maybe just relieved she hadn't been dragged away for the amusement of some barbarian brute.

Silus grabbed his arm.

'Silus!' Odo embraced him, squeezed hard. The boy was not drunk. That was a small mercy. Silus prised Odo's arms off him, and gripped his shoulders.

'Odo, where is your father? Where is your brother?'

Odo frowned in puzzlement. 'I don't know. Father took Ewald and went to talk to his cousin. I stayed here because...' He looked at the slave girl and reddened.

Silus looked across to Caracalla, then around at the soldiers. They were in position now, ready, waiting patiently. There was no time.

'Listen to me. I have a very important mission. It's vital to the safety of Rome and the Alamanni. But you must come with me right now. Understand?'

'Of course. What is it?'

'No time to explain. Follow me.'

Silus gripped Odo's wrist, and dragged him through the warriors, east towards the river.

Some of the Germans noticed the legionaries now, and looked around in puzzlement, pointing them out to their colleagues. An uneasy murmur rippled through the air.

'Silus, what's going on?'

'Shut up. Keep moving.'

They reached the periphery of the throng, near the river. The bank sloped gently until reaching a steep edge, a ravine cut into the soil and rock. Only a few Alamanni had come this far from the party, most of them to urinate, defaecate, vomit, or fornicate. All of them now were looking towards the arrayed legionaries, their armour glinting as the sun broke through the scattered cloud. They pointed and muttered, their stances uneasy.

They reached the edge of the ravine, and Silus looked over a ten-foot drop into deep, fast-flowing water. He turned back and saw, in the distance, Caracalla draw his sword and raise it above his head. The murmuring raised in pitch as the consternation increased.

'Silus, I don't like this,' said Odo. 'We should go back. My father...'

Caracalla swung his sword down in a slashing motion, and with a roar, the legionaries broke into a run.

There was instant chaos. The vulnerable Germans, weaponless and armoured only in linen and wool, ran in all directions at once. Some, the majority, ran towards the swords. Others ran away, searching for family and friends, or simply in blind panic. There was no leadership. None of the elders or warleaders imposed their authority on the mob. Silus suddenly understood his mission to assassinate Suabgast. Maybe he could have organised the Alamanni with their large numbers to fight back, even unarmed as they were. But there was now no one present with the authority and the force of will to turn these individual warriors into an army.

Odo was staring in disbelief.

'Silus, I don't understand. Why are they doing this?'

Silus thought he knew. Caracalla saw the Alamanni as a threat, a cooperation between traditionally uncooperative tribes, who now possessed the numbers and power to threaten Rome. Like the Marcomanni two generations before. Like the Caledonians and Maeatae only a couple of years ago. Caracalla was eliminating the threat, and he was doing it in a way that maximised his chances and minimised his costs.

The first line of legionaries crashed into the warriors charging against them. The angry shouts and jeers changed instantly to screams and howls. Gladii stabbed, piercing soft flesh, withdrawing, stabbing again. Interlocked shields formed an impenetrable wall that the barbarians broke against. Bodies fell, were trampled as the line of legionaries advanced, the rear lines stabbing down to finish off the wounded.

Here and there, a solitary, brave German, or a handful working together, managed to tear a shield away, to grab a spear or sword and turn it on their treacherous attackers. Such resistance was fleeting, the courageous fighters cut down within moments.

Silus looked at Odo. He was still as a rabbit before a fox. His face was pale, his mouth an O.

'Father,' he whispered. 'Ewald.'

And then, without warning, his paralysis broke, and he darted forward.

Silus caught his arm.

'No, Odo.'

Odo struggled, but in his shock and panic was ineffectual, and Silus kept his grip firm. 'Odo, you can't do anything. You can't save them.'

Silus' words had the opposite effect than intended. Odo's struggles redoubled, and he kicked back into Silus' shin, a painful thrust with his heel that felt like it had come close to shattering the bone. Silus cried out and his grip loosened. Odo pulled himself free, made to run. Silus dived on him, wrestling him to the ground.

'Get off me. Get off me, curse you.' His fists beat against Silus, no real strength behind them, but enough to make it hard for Silus to keep control.

'I'm sorry,' said Silus. Then he punched Odo hard in the side of the head.

There wasn't sufficient force to knock him unconscious – a blow of that power could as easily kill as knock someone out. But it was enough to daze him, subdue the youngster. Odo went limp, struggling weakly. Silus lifted himself off his young friend and looked around. The small number of Alamanni who had been nearby had scattered, some towards the battle, some away. A few had dived into the river and were swimming away. Silus picked Odo up in his arms and carried him to the ravine. He sat him, still stuporous, on the edge, and slapped him lightly around the face.

Odo's eyes focused, and he stared at Silus in dazed confusion.

'Can you swim?'

'You son of a cheap whore,' said Odo, voice slurred. 'Liar. Betrayer!'

'I'll take that as a yes.' He pushed Odo firmly, and the young boy toppled over the edge with a cry, cut off as he disappeared into the freezing water. Silus watched for a moment that seemed to drag out, until his friend, who now hated him, surfaced, waving his arms and spluttering.

Silus gave him a sad wave. 'I really am sorry.' He watched for a moment longer, then turned his back and walked towards the carnage.

Chapter Fourteen

Caracalla watched the scene unfold below him. He was seated astride his favourite horse, Bucephalus. Beside him sat Macrinus, who stared in fascination at the slaughter, and Festus, who looked uncomfortable.

Caracalla felt only triumph. His advisors and spies were vague about the origins of these Alamanni, but Caracalla knew his history. He knew that, regardless of how they felt towards Rome at that moment in time, that attitude would change, and they would turn on the Empire, just like so many German nations, and nations at other borders, had done in the past.

When his spies had told him that the Alamanni were growing in strength and number, he had known he must destroy them. There were other tribes in Germania that were more overtly hostile, like the Chatti, and some, Oclatinius for example, had counselled that he should accept the Alamanni offer of alliance in order to destroy those other tribes first. But others, such as Festus and Macrinus, had aligned with his fears of leaving an enemy at his back when campaigning deep in Germania. Arminius, the architect of the disaster in the Teutoburg forest, had left a long legacy, and the fear of betrayal from German so-called allies ran deep. Better to be the betrayer than the betrayed.

So he had hatched this plan with the help of Festus, Macrinus, and a reluctant Oclatinius. And now he watched it unfold to perfection. The flower of Alamanni youth was being hacked down before his eyes, their sap draining into the earth. He knew that this was not their entire manpower, he could not hope for that, but it was a fatal blow. They would not be able to resist the legions after today.

Two legionaries approached, dragging an unresisting captive between them. They threw him to the floor at Caracalla's feet. When the man looked up, Caracalla recognised the bloodied features of Chnodomar. The chief's face was streaked with dirt and tears. He was bleeding from a cut above his eye, and from one ear. He was trembling violently.

'Why?' he cried out plaintively.

Caracalla shrugged. 'You were a threat.'

'You promised. We trusted you.'

'A promise to your kind is meaningless. There is no dishonour in breaking your oath when it is given to a barbarian. And I know that for all your words of peace and friendship, you will fall on us like wild dogs when our back is turned. Your Arminius taught us that.'

'Not our Arminius. He was Cherusci. Not Alamanni.'

'You're all Germans, all barbarians.'

'You're evil. You will be cursed, by your gods and mine.'

Caracalla looked out over the slaughter, his face displaying a satisfied half-smile.

'Take a look, Chnodomar, at your people. They are broken. They will never trouble Rome again.'

Chnodomar turned. There was no resistance now. Just attempts to flee, pleas for mercy, and murder of the wounded and those attempting to surrender.

'I am looking, great Emperor. And I see a people foully wronged. Who will rise again, and make Rome pay for this treachery.'

'Maybe. But not for a generation or more.'

'We are not all you see before you now. There are still many of our tribe in our homes and farms.'

'A trivial problem, now we have crushed the majority of your warriors.'

'Maybe. But when you descend on our homes and our families, our men will die with honour. When you die, whether it is tomorrow or three score years from now, you will die as a man hated, your name cursed forever.'

This struck home. Reputation was all, to Caracalla. He was the Emperor of Rome. The conqueror of Caledonia. Soon to be conqueror of Germania and Parthia. The new Alexander.

He turned to Macrinus.

'Kill him.'

Macrinus dismounted smoothly, drew his sword and thrust it through Chnodomar's neck, skewering him from front to back. Chnodomar's hands flew to the blade, clutched it with eyes and mouth wide, then he toppled over sideways.

Caracalla returned to surveying the carnage, but his pleasure at the day's events was tarnished. He wheeled his horse, and accompanied by Festus, Macrinus and his guards, he rode for Colonia.

–

Silus picked his way through the bodies. There were so many, many dead, and the enormity of his task nearly overwhelmed him. But he had to do this. For Odo. For Ada. For Ima.

He saw a man with a broken spear protruding from his back, who was about Boda's build. He turned him over, and let out his breath. The sightless eyes staring back at him did not belong to Odo's father. He let the body flop back.

Most of the fighting was finished. The legionaries had broken formation now, and had started the grisly business of executing the survivors. Centurions were organising teams of soldiers to bring prisoners forward in groups, pushing them to their knees, then efficiently dispatching them with a thrust downwards between collarbone and neck. Some went meekly to their deaths, some cursing and struggling, but the end was the same for all.

Other teams of soldiers were checking bodies, just like Silus, except with a different purpose. Any flickers of life, they extinguished with sword or spear. Silus found himself hurrying, desperately trying to find Boda and Ewald before the execution squads got to them.

Two legionaries approached him menacingly, swords drawn, and Silus realised that they must be thinking that anyone who wasn't in armour must be a barbarian.

'Stand down,' he said, in his best command voice. 'I'm Gaius Sergius Silus, centurion of the Arcani.'

They looked him up and down doubtfully. Silus put a hand on the knife at his belt and took a step forward.

'Do I have to say it twice?' he growled. 'Fuck off.'

The men backed away, and Silus resumed his search. He was near to giving up hope when he saw a familiar face.

Familiar, but dead. Boda, father to his friend, and to his last lover, who had invited him into his house and treated him as a treasured guest, lay with eyes wide open, blood coming from a gash in his head that looked like it had been made with a shield edge, and another wound in his chest, the finishing blow. Silus knelt beside him, and bowed his head.

Then he saw movement from a nearby body, a dozen yards away. Just the slightest motion of an arm. A young boy, sprawled on his front, his face sideways, facing Silus, eyes closed.

Ewald. And he was alive. Just.

But others had seen the movement too. Three legionaries who had been stripping some jewellery from a dead chief noticed, and approached. One drew his sword.

Silus leapt to his feet, cried out, ran forward. The legionary ignored him and thrust downwards.

Silus barreled into him, knocking him sideways in a two-arm tackle around his torso. The other legionaries stared in surprise for a moment, and Silus rolled to his feet as the downed man gasped breath into his winded lungs.

The two standing legionaries closed shoulder to shoulder, swords in hands.

Silus put a warning hand up. 'Gaius Sergius Silus of the Arcani.'

They paused, doubtful as their comrades had been.

'Why did you attack Sextus?' said one.

Sextus was sitting up, looking offended.

'I need this one alive,' Silus said, gesturing to Ewald, who was stirring weakly.

'Why?' asked the same legionary.

In two swift steps, Silus was inside the surprised legionary's guard, with his blade at his throat.

'Did you not hear me the first time?' hissed Silus. 'I am Arcani. There should be no further questions.'

'We meant no insult, sir,' said the other legionary. 'We'll leave you be.'

Silus stepped back, nodded, then said, 'No. Help me. This boy is an informant. I need to get him back into German territory. Help me get him to the river.'

The legionaries looked at each other in annoyance, no doubt thinking about all the loot they would be missing out on. But they had seen Silus move, and had no wish to get on the wrong side of an Arcanus. They muttered reluctant acquiescence.

Silus bent over Ewald. The boy had a deep wound in his outer thigh, and a bruise on his head. He was semi-conscious, and when Silus lifted him upright, he began to moan incoherently. He gave him some water, and Ewald sipped, coughed and sipped again.

'Get your shield under him, come on.'

They wiggled the curved shield beneath Ewald, and two of them hoisted him up. His legs and arms dangled over the sides, but it was better than throwing him over a shoulder. As they headed towards the river, they got sideways looks from the various legionaries patrolling and prowling around the battlefield. A centurion challenged them, and the legionaries looked to Silus to reply.

'Business of the Arcani,' said Silus. 'Nothing to do with you, centurion. Carry on.'

The centurion watched them pass suspiciously, but said nothing more.

The carrion crows had already begun to settle. Where there were unmoving corpses, and no legionaries nearby, they started their grisly work. First they went for the softest parts, the bits of the body that required little effort. The eyeballs. The tongue. Only then would they start on the tougher parts, the meat and gristle.

Silus watched as one bird dipped its head into the eye socket of a young slave girl, caught up in the slaughter. It pulled back, a slimy string of goo dangling from its beak. A larger bird came over to challenge for the morsel, and they fought and squawked at each other briefly, before the smaller bird flapped away, looking for uncontested food. There was plenty to go around.

They reached the river, and Silus had the grumbling legionaries walk along the bank until they found a path down the steep ravine to the water. Then they had to find some way to cross, and he sent them scouting up and down to find some form of transport.

Of course, almost everything that floated had been commandeered by the fleeing Alamanni who had made it to the river. But one of the legionaries returned, looking pleased with himself, and pointed out a makeshift raft of half a dozen logs lashed together, stuck a little way out in the flow, on which lay a dead warrior. Presumably he had only got so far before succumbing to his injuries.

Silus got the legionaries to help him wade out into the fast-moving water with Ewald, position him on the raft, and get it free from the rocks it had stuck on. They looked worried that he was going to ask them to help him cross as well, but now he just wanted rid of them. He dismissed them with cursory thanks and instructions to give him a good shove. Gratefully they did as they were told, and even as he floated free into the main stream of the river, they were rushing back to the battlefield, hoping there was still good stuff left that was worth stealing.

The raft swirled in the currents, and Silus found himself pointing forward, then back. The motion made him feel nauseous, and he didn't attempt to row, content for the river to bear him and Ewald far from the scene of the slaughter.

After they had travelled some distance, he grabbed a long stick that was floating nearby, and used it to fend off rocks, and slowly edge the raft towards the far bank. Eventually, it nudged up against a shallow beach in a river bend, and he was able to drag the raft half out of the water, and then lift Ewald off. Out of the motion of the river, he was better able to assess the boy's injuries. Nothing that seemed likely to kill him. At least not yet. If infection set in, who knew? He bound the wound in the boy's leg with a strip of cloth from his tunic, and then lightly tapped his cheeks.

Ewald's eyes slowly focused on Silus.

'You.' He coughed.

'Can you walk?'

'Did you… save me?'

Silus supposed so. But it didn't feel like it. Not when it was his side that had done this in the first place. He put an arm around Ewald's chest and lifted him to his feet. Though he had to support most of his weight, he was able to get Ewald walking, east, towards the forests.

It was slow going, and they had to stop frequently as Ewald fatigued easily. Silus reflected on the irony that so recently he was helping someone escape in the opposite direction. They didn't speak. Maybe Ewald was too out of breath, or too traumatised. Whatever, the reason, Silus was grateful for it.

After some time they reached a copse, and Silus guided Ewald into the trees, and into a clearing in the centre.

Half a dozen Alamanni glared at him as he approached. They were slumped in a rough circle, a variety of ages, from one Ewald's years to one older than Boda. Two bore wounds, and one of them, who was lying recumbent and staring at the sky, looked like he would not last much longer. The others had obviously fled when they saw the first signs of trouble. Maybe they would not be feted as the bravest of their tribes. But they were alive.

None were armed, but there was an air of menace hanging over them, and Silus did not want a fight. He lowered Ewald to the ground and spread his hands in front of him, to show he was holding no weapon and meant no harm. They watched him in silence.

Silus pointed at Ewald. 'Alamanni. Yours.'

They looked at Ewald but said nothing.

'Ewald,' said Silus. 'Tell them.'

Ewald took a breath and spoke in Germanic. Silus watched their faces as they listened, looking from Ewald to Silus. Their expressions softened from outright hostility to mere glowering suspicion and resentment. The oldest replied to Ewald, and they conversed in their guttural language for a few moments. Then Ewald spoke to Silus.

'They will take me home,' he said. 'They are resting because of the injured one. But they will continue soon.'

Silus nodded, thankful. 'Tell them not to delay. I don't know if Caracalla intends to hunt down the survivors, but knowing how he works, it wouldn't surprise me. He isn't the sort to squander any advantage.'

'I will. Silus. You are a Roman. Why did you save me?'

Because of Odo. Because of their sister. Because it was wrong. But he couldn't bring himself to say anything, so he just shrugged, pathetically.

'Silus. My father. My brother.'

'I took Odo to safety before it all started,' he said.

Ewald was not stupid, and immediately noted the obvious omission.

'Then my father…?'

Silus shook his head.

Ewald looked down, swallowed. He held his tears inside. Maybe that's what he thought bravery was.

'Please pass on my condolences to your mother and sister. I don't know if they will believe it, but I am truly sorry. And when you see your brother…' He trailed off. Odo would never forgive him, not just for the treachery of Silus' Emperor, but for his own deceit, taking Odo away from danger without giving him the chance to save his father. There was nothing he could say that would make that right.

'Look after yourself,' he said, the words sounding weak even in his own ears. He turned, feeling the eyes of Ewald and the other Alamanni burning into the back of his head, and walked back towards the Empire.

–

Silus stormed into the governor's palace, past the guards, growling at them when they challenged him that he was on Arcani business, and they could go fuck themselves. It was enough for them to let him pass, but the German bodyguards at the entrance to Caracalla's headquarters were less impressed by his credentials, and barred his way with crossed spears.

'Let me pass.' His voice held all the authority he could muster, but his anger was plain to see, and the Emperor's personal bodyguard took their jobs seriously. They blocked the doorway impassively.

Silus put his hand on the hilt of his sword. 'This is your only warning,' he said. 'Stand aside.'

It was like talking to the wall of Hadrianus. As impassive and impenetrable. But walls were no obstacle to an Arcanus. He began to draw his gladius.

A hand clamped over his wrist, held it fast, the blade only half drawn. He turned and found himself staring into the stern features of Oclatinius.

'What do you think you are doing?'

'Take your hand away.'

Oclatinius' grip was surprisingly firm. Silus took a step backwards, wrenching himself free.

'Don't get in my way, old man.'

With speed that amazed Silus and took him completely by surprise, Oclatinius jabbed him with straight fingers beneath the ribs. His breath left him, and he doubled up. Oclatinius stuck two fingers into the angle behind his jaw, under his ear, and Silus was overwhelmed with pain and dizziness.

Oclatinius spoke to the guards in a low, threatening tone.

'You saw nothing here. Do you understand?'

They nodded, clearly more intimidated by the old man than they were by Silus. Oclatinius grabbed Silus' upper arm and dragged him away.

When they reached a secluded office, Oclatinius threw Silus at a stool.

'Sit,' he barked.

All the fight departed from him. Silus slumped onto the wooden seat.

'In the name of Mithras, what did you think you were doing?'

Silus had no answer. He had let his feelings overwhelm him, and that alone would earn Oclatinius' disapprobation. His plan had gone no further than confronting Caracalla and telling him what he thought of him. And then what? The guards tried to cut him down, and he either died, or killed them. Then did he need to kill the Emperor too? Or try to flee? Or wait meekly for his arrest? What would happen to Tituria then?

He put his head in his hands and began to shake. Oclatinius said nothing, and waited for the flood of emotion to subside. After a while, Silus took a deep breath and looked up at Oclatinius.

'How could you let it happen?' The anger had gone from his voice now. His tone wasn't even accusatory. He was genuinely puzzled.

Oclatinius spoke with clear regret. 'You overestimate my influence. Others have the ear of the Emperor more than I do.'

'Festus?'

'For one. And Macrinus. They are not the type of people to tell Caracalla something he doesn't want to hear.'

'And you are?'

Oclatinius inclined his head. 'It is a habit that could serve me badly, if I wasn't so valuable to him.'

'So you tried to uphold the honour of Rome, at least.'

'You misunderstand me,' said Oclatinius. 'My opposition to this mad plan was not based on honour. It was strategy. The Germans are a tough nut to crack. Many have come unstuck on them in the past, and any victories have been temporary. We had the opportunity to split their forces, use the Alamanni to crush the Chatti and the others in the north and east. Then we could deal with the Alamanni at a later date. Or assimilate them into the Empire, which I have a suspicion might have happened over time if we carried on with trade and friendly relations. Much of Rome's Empire has been gained by conquest, but also much by peaceable treaties, and inheriting lands bequeathed by chiefs and kings. The tragedy of today is that it was all so... unnecessary.'

'Then why did he do it?'

'Caracalla has a keen eye for an advantage, however it is gained. He defeated a powerful force with the potential to be a formidable enemy, with almost no loss.'

'And has earned their perpetual hatred.'

Oclatinius inclined his head in agreement.

'So. What now?'

'Now,' said Oclatinius. 'It is war.'

Chapter Fifteen

Caracalla was only half listening. The day after the battle, and he still had that feeling inside, that sensation of joy, like the first time he had sex, the first time he killed a man in combat. It was his first victory. The first that was his alone, undisputed. Though he knew that he was responsible for the triumph in Caledonia, that he had earned the title Britannicus, he was aware that some muttered the victory belonged to his father, that he was just a lieutenant. There could be no disputing the architect of yesterday's result. No father to overshadow him, no brother to undermine him.

Thoughts of Geta threatened to crowd in on him, to burst the bubble of his exaltation, so he pushed them aside, and tried to concentrate on the discussions of his advisors. They were poring over scouting reports of the movements of the Chatti and other tribes from around the mouth of the Albis river. Festus relayed some information from one of his spies, and the others nodded and commented.

Julia was present, and he kept glancing at her. She kept her eyes from him, steadfastly ignoring his attempts to make eye contact. It had been some time since they had shared a bed. She had shown no interest, but ultimately it had been his choice. He had not wanted to see his brother's accusing eyes staring out of her beautiful face as he looked down at her.

Now, though, he felt different. There was a virility coursing through him, and he felt more aroused than he had for some time. He looked at the curve of her body under her stola, thought about times they had spent together before, and his breath quickened. He blinked hard and forced himself to look away. Festus' ugly face helped dampen his ardour, at least temporarily. The Commander of the Sacred Bedchamber was speaking, and Caracalla focused on his words.

'The Alamanni are shattered. We need to march into their territory, now, and wipe them out, before they have a chance to pull their pieces back together.'

Oclatinius looked grave. 'Maybe we should be magnanimous in our victory. If we extend an olive branch now, then, though we cannot expect their forgiveness, at least maybe we will not be nurturing a new enemy on our doorstep. And the time may come when Rome has need of allies.'

Macrinus shook his head vigorously. 'Nonsense. Rome needs no allies. These barbarians only understand might. The Caledonians and Maeatae will not be troubling Rome for a generation or more, after your father's wise policy of extermination, Augustus. Let it be the same with the Alamanni.'

Caracalla gritted his teeth. Always his father. His shade still blocked the sun. No more.

'These people and their lands are mine. This victory is mine. Macrinus, send orders for the men to prepare. Tomorrow we march.'

His advisors, recognising a final word, bowed their heads and hurried out. Julia made to leave as well.

'Stay, Julia,' said Caracalla.

'Yes, Augustus,' said Julia, submissively. When the others had left, and the door had closed behind them, he walked up to her. He looked into her face for a moment, then brushed the hair back from her forehead.

'Still beautiful.'

'You are very kind, Augustus.' She spoke with the dutiful expression of a slave, without warmth or love. Maybe another day, that would have put him off, and he would have looked for a favourite servant to satisfy him. But not today. Today, he felt like the ruler of the world. He was Alexander reborn.

He took her arm, and led her towards his bedchamber. If he took her from behind, he reflected, he wouldn't see those eyes.

The sun was gently warming and the moderate breeze was cool. A pleasant temperature for hiking in the German hinterland. Scattered around the hills and valleys were the first flowers of spring, narcissi and daffodils, and the calmly grazing goats, sheep and cattle, tended by herding boys, gave the countryside an idyllic air.

Many miles behind them marched Caracalla and the legions, armed, armoured and bent on bringing destruction to this bucolic scene.

Silus and Atius had been assigned to track the movements of the fleeing Alamanni, and find out where their remaining strength was gathered. They weren't the only scouts performing the mission, but they were the two most familiar with the region. And of course, they could no longer expect help from the Alamanni who had been working with them. Silus had had no chance to argue with

Oclatinius before being sent back into the field. Maybe the old man didn't want to give him time to think. Nor had he had a chance to argue against Atius as his partner. Oclatinius had simply told him how it was to be, and dismissed him.

Silus and Atius spoke to each other professionally, pointing out tracks and other tell-tale signs of the passing of significant numbers of men. They discussed their locations, their bearings. They coordinated their scouting, and informed each other when they saw Germans – farmers, warriors, women and children – so they could avoid them. They had nothing else to say to each other.

As yet there was no sign of any reorganisation of the fled survivors, just scattered, broken warriors fleeing east to safety. Silus was aware at the back of his mind that he was still aiding the Emperor who had behaved so treacherously. But he was a Roman. As Oclatinius had said, this was war, and the lives of many Roman soldiers depended on the quality of the reconnaissance that they performed. And much as he loved Odo, when it came to a choice between the lives of Romans and barbarians, Silus, a loyal Roman citizen, would choose his compatriots every time. At least, that's what he told himself.

Atius pointed to something in the middle distance, an object against a tree. They headed towards it to investigate, and as they approached it became clear it was a body. A warrior, young, long hair tied back, tunic torn. Silus knelt by him and inspected the corpse. A fly, buzzing loudly, flew out of his mouth, making Silus jerk back involuntarily. More flies hovered around the warrior's midriff, and Silus saw a wound in the side of his abdomen, congealed and sticky. The entry hole wasn't large, but there was a putrid odour, worse than he would expect just from a day or so of decay. The blade must have ruptured his guts. A slow, agonising way to die.

He rose to his feet, and avoided looking at Atius, who said, 'I wonder what Caracalla will do if we don't find a concentration of the enemy.'

'I think you know what he will do,' said Silus. 'He will make a wasteland. Then he will move on. It's like a plague of locusts, but ones that aren't hungry, that just have the urge to destroy.'

'They are a threat,' said Atius, and Silus knew the words rang hollow in Atius' own ears.

'Is that what you told yourself? All that time, when you knew what was going to happen? All that time you kept it to yourself, a secret from me, your partner and best friend?'

'I... didn't know what to do. I was going to tell you. I wanted to, more than anything, to share the burden. You always know what to do.'

'But you didn't.'

'Then I saw how you were with Odo. How much you trusted him, liked him. And I knew Odo would be one of the ones to die.'

'I thought you hated him just because your own guide had betrayed you and you thought he would do the same.'

'I know. I let you believe that. But that wasn't the reason I behaved with him the way I did. It's because I was ashamed.'

Silus turned now and looked his friend in the face. Silus' eyes were wide and wet.

'You should have told me,' said Silus, his voice rising.

'And what would you have done?'

'Tried to stop it somehow!' Silus was almost shouting now.

'Exactly. For all the things you have done for Caracalla, he gives you a lot of leeway. The same with Oclatinius. But there are limits. If you had tried to interfere with this plan, spoken out of turn to the Emperor, or worse, tried to warn the Alamanni, then Caracalla would have ordered Oclatinius to kill you and he would have done it in a heartbeat.'

Silus stared, searching for words, none coming.

'You risked your life, on the chance I might have been alive,' said Atius. Tears were running freely down his still hollow cheeks now. Silus hadn't seen Atius cry since he had rescued him. Sullen, irritable, distant, yes. But not tearful. 'You saved me. So I gave up my honour to save you.'

The anger inside Silus did not disappear. But it attenuated a little. He would not give his approval of Atius' actions. He would not absolve him of his wrongdoing. He could pray to his Christos for that.

But he could try to move on. He gave Atius a curt nod. 'Tracks head this way. Let's see where they lead.'

–

The trail led them east and south, along the north bank of the Menus, a large river that eventually merged with the Rhenus. The scattered tracks slowly coalesced. Silus pictured droplets of rain gathered in an upturned shield, which when you rocked it in gentle circles slowly came together to make a single pool of drinkable water. The Alamanni were congregating.

They spent the night in a hollow they dug out below a fallen trunk. They huddled together for warmth – though it was spring, a frost still descended and rimed the leaf litter and the new buds on the trees. They did not return to their argument. That abscess had been lanced, and now picking at it would slow the healing. And there was still a lot of healing to be done.

But they did talk. They talked about drinking beer when they were back in Colonia. They talked about returning to Rome. They reminisced about missions and battles of times past. And they slept, closer than they had been for a year. Still, Silus thought something had broken in their friendship. He wondered if it would ever become whole again.

The next morning they ate a breakfast of hard biscuit and dried meat in something closer to a companiable quiet than an icy silence. They were on the move before the sun had crested the horizon. Almost immediately they began to encounter small groups of warriors. The Arcani's dress was purposefully nondescript, and from a distance they could pass for Alamanni, although that disguise would be useless the moment someone tried to speak to them in Germanic. But they kept their distance, waved greetings where it seemed appropriate, and stayed off the beaten path as best they could.

The concentrations of warriors became ever greater as the day wore on. Though they were some way off, Silus could make out their attitudes from their stance, their gait, their noise. Some were sullen, shoulders hunched, feet shuffling. Survivors of the massacre no doubt. Others were angry, voices raised, stride purposeful. Maybe relatives or friends of those who died. And some were enthusiastic, laughing and singing war songs and wrestling each other playfully. Men unaffected by Caracalla's treachery, but excited by the prospect of battle.

It was becoming clear in which direction the gathering warriors were headed now, and Silus and Atius plotted a route that would take them into the general vicinity while keeping far enough away for at least some degree of comfort and safety. Towards the mid-afternoon, the trail of the warriors curved around the foot of a steep hill. Silus gestured to the summit.

'Let's get up there and take a look.'

The hill was rocky and steep, and in places they had to use handholds to haul themselves up. By the time they reached the top, they were breathless and sweating, despite the cool air. The far side of the hill had collapsed into a scree slope, and they stood at the edge and looked down. Atius whistled.

'Christos, there are a lot of them.'

Silus nodded. 'If Caracalla thinks he got them all, he's very wrong.'

Below them, in a large valley, were thousands upon thousands of men. They milled around, looking like tiny mice swarming over a grain store. Silus squinted, trying to make out detail. He thought he could see a variety of tribal colours decorating shields, but it wasn't easy from this distance. It made sense though. The Alamanni was a confederacy, and no doubt after the massacre they had put out the call far and wide to gather, and avenge their slain kin. The warriors below would be everyone that the Alamanni could draw into one place. Farmers, young boys, even some of the more fearsome women. And allies of course, other Germans who were not part of the confederacy, but who knew their fate was bound up with the Alamanni. The Germans might be barbarians, but they weren't stupid. They knew how Rome in general, and Caracalla in particular, behaved. This was a fight for their very survival.

'How many do you think?' asked Silus.

Atius put his hand to his eyes to shield them from the low sun. His lips moved as he counted rows and columns, and did the mathematics in his head.

'I make it around twenty thousand,' he said eventually. 'Probably a quarter of them mounted.'

'I came up with something similar,' said Silus. 'How many men does Caracalla have with him?'

'Oclatinius told me one legion and a couple of cohorts of the Praetorians. Around six thousand. The rest of the army is advancing in two columns northwards, to surround the Alamanni territory and cut off any escape deeper into Germania Magna.'

Silus shook his head. 'It's not enough. Even with Roman superiority in weapons and discipline, six thousand won't stand against twenty thousand, especially not if they are surprised. And that army down there looks ready to march. We need to get back and warn them.'

They scrambled down the hillside, half of the time on their backsides, and reached the bottom with a dozen bumps and scrapes and one painfully twisted ankle between them. Silus put a hand on Atius' shoulder to support him and Atius moved his foot in experimental circles.

'Are you sound?'

'Hurts like buggery, but I can walk on it.'

They turned and saw two Alamanni riders trotting up to them.

Silus and Atius exchanged glances, then Silus put a hand up in greeting. The riders approached, slowing down as they neared. Both had spears under their arms, pointing downwards, but ready for use if needed. They pulled up next to the two Arcani and looked down at them suspiciously. One spoke to Silus in deep Germanic dialect.

Silus looked at Atius questioningly. Atius shrugged. 'Not a clue.'

Simultaneously, the two Arcani reached forward and each grabbed the spear of one of the riders, just behind the head. They yanked towards them, and both the Alamanni horsemen were jerked off their mounts. They fell heavily to the floor, letting out oofs of breath as they landed.

The rider that Atius had accosted lost his grip on the spear as he fell. Atius quickly reversed it, and before he even had time to breathe in, Atius had skewered him, the spear penetrating his ribcage and pinning him to the earth. The barbarian's hand gripped the shaft tightly, then his grip went limp and he fell back.

Silus wasn't so lucky. His rider had fallen better, and had kept a grip on his weapon. They wrestled, rolling in the damp earth for mastery of the spear. The barbarian, heavier than Silus, ended up on top of him. He held the spear shaft across Silus' neck and pressed. Silus pushed back, but the wood bore down, squashing his throat. Silus tried to gasp and found his windpipe constricted. He struggled desperately, panic rising as he fought for air. He was losing, and he suddenly felt that this was his moment, this was when he would die.

The pressure was suddenly gone. The warrior toppled sideways. Silus stared at him. Silus' attacker had a different spear transfixing his neck from side to side. Silus sat up and looked at Atius, a dozen paces away. Silus tried to speak, swallowed and tried again. The words were hoarse.

'Good throw.'

Atius walked over and held out his hand to help Silus to his feet.

'I thought I was gone there,' said Silus. 'You saved my life.'

Atius looked down, uncharacteristically bashful. 'It's what we do, isn't it?'

'Yes,' said Silus. 'I suppose it is.'

He grabbed the reins of one of the riderless horses, who had been skittishly watching the fight play out. Atius took hold of the other. 'Let's get back to Caracalla,' said Silus. 'I don't know if he deserves the warning, but those men following him certainly do.'

Chapter Sixteen

Caracalla looked Silus up and down suspiciously.

'You're sure?'

'Yes, Augustus. Atius and I counted independently and came up with the same figure. About twenty thousand.'

'And a quarter of them cavalry?'

'Yes, Augustus.'

'They are mistaken,' said Macrinus with a dismissive wave. 'It's not possible. We killed almost all of them. There were few survivors.'

'Germania is a big place,' said Oclatinius. 'And they would not have given us all their men to go and fight the Chatti. They would have kept some in reserve, to protect themselves against other tribes taking advantage of the absence of fighting men. Not to mention those tending the herds and flocks, and those too young or old to fight in normal circumstances. Now they will have called on every last man, because they know if they lose this next battle, they will be destroyed utterly.'

Macrinus glared at Oclatinius, but Caracalla looked thoughtful.

'Oclatinius is right,' said Caracalla. 'We should have considered this.' He looked at Macrinus and Festus. 'Why didn't you warn me of this possibility?'

Festus and Macrinus looked at each other, suddenly alarmed as the Emperor's fierce attention was turned on them. Macrinus flushed, and Festus opened his mouth and stuttered. Silus wondered if Festus and Macrinus had genuinely thought that the massacre would break all Alamanni resistance, or if maybe they wanted Caracalla to suffer a defeat to undermine his position. If it was the former they were fools; if it was the latter they were traitors. But Caracalla merely turned back to Oclatinius. When his attention was no longer on them, Silus noticed Festus and Macrinus exchange a look which could have been anger, or could have been something deeper and more sinister.

'How long until the other legions arrive?' asked Caracalla.

'Messengers have been sent. They are marching double time, and will be here tomorrow afternoon.'

'And the Alamanni?'

'They will be on us in the morning.'

Caracalla stroked his beard, and the deep lines in his forehead became ravines.

'Then we must find a way to delay them.'

'We are well-defended in our marching camp,' said Macrinus. 'We just hold on here.'

'It's not enough,' said Oclatinius. 'These men are angry and scared and fighting for their very survival. They will overwhelm our defences long before the rest of the army gets here.'

'Then what do you suggest?' snapped Macrinus.

'I have an idea,' said Oclatinius.

–

'I'm going to need you two scouting our flanks,' said Oclatinius. Silus and Atius stood before him in his tent, near the centre of the marching camp. 'You have both moved far beyond mere reconnaissance missions, but we need every man we can spare in the battle, which includes all the speculatores, exploratores and frumentarii. You two are too valuable to put in the front line, so you will make sure there are no nasty surprises.'

Silus looked doubtful.

'What is it, Silus? Speak up.'

'I don't want to do this.'

'Venus' sweet ass, why can't you just follow orders?'

Silus shuffled his feet but looked Oclatinius in the eye. 'I made friends with the Alamanni. They saved my life. I don't want to fight.'

Oclatinius rolled his eyes. 'I could just tell you to do as you are fucking well told,' he said. 'And yet here I am, wasting my precious time persuading you to do your job. Listen, Silus. You are scouting. Not fighting. You will watch for surprise attacks. You will warn me if you see anything unexpected. That's it. I won't force you to offend your precious conscience – a luxury, mind you, that not all of us can afford – by risking hurting one of these barbarians that you believe you have formed a bond with.'

'Thank you, sir,' said Silus. 'I accept my mission.'

'How gracious of you.' Oclatinius' voice dripped with irony.

'I want to fight,' said Atius.

'Mars give me strength. What?'

'Put me at the front,' said Atius.

'Atius, what are you talking about?' Silus felt alarm rising inside him. He had risked so much to bring his friend back from captivity, to save him from death and torture, and now he wanted to throw it away.

'Silus, I need this. They held me for so long. They did things, things that made me feel... no longer a man.'

'It wasn't the Alamanni. That was the Chatti.'

'They are all the same. Can't you see that? They speak the same language, have the same customs, look the same, share the same blood. If Caracalla hadn't betrayed them today, they would have betrayed us tomorrow. You may not like what he did, but it was shrewd, clever, and in the best interests of Rome.'

'Don't do this,' said Silus. 'I don't want you to...' His voice trailed off. He didn't want him to what? To kill Alamanni? To try to heal his wounds with the blood of others? 'I don't want you to die.'

Atius gave him a half-smile and put a hand on his shoulder. 'I have no intention of joining Christos in heaven any time soon, friend. But I need to do this.'

Silus put his hand over Atius' and squeezed. He gave a single nod.

'How touching,' scoffed Oclatinius. 'Fine, Atius, if you insist on putting yourself in harm's way, I'll find a place for you. Silus can do the scouting job on his own.'

Impulsively, Silus threw his arms around Atius. Atius hugged him back.

'Be safe, friend,' said Silus.

'You too,' said Atius.

'Vesta's tits,' swore Oclatinius, and stomped away.

—

'This is tantamount to treason,' protested Festus. 'To put the Imperial body in such acute danger...'

'Stop fussing,' snapped Caracalla, as he was fastened into his armour. 'This is glorious. Worthy of Alexander himself.' He rolled his shoulders, and swished his sword around him. His upper arm muscles bulged impressively, the rope-like veins running over them standing out. He was no weakling, far from it, and he was skilled in single combat. But fighting was only ever the back-up plan.

'He will be in no danger,' said Oclatinius. 'We've been through this. The new warleader of the Alamanni will most certainly be Chlodulf, the older cousin of Chnodomar. He is elderly, and by all accounts sickly, which is why he did not attend the... ah... peace conference, but he is the most senior of those surviving. He cannot accept an offer of single combat. His council would forbid it, even if he felt his honour demanded it. They could not watch everything be thrown away because an old man wanted to fight.'

'And while they debate it,' said Caracalla, 'and I parade in front of their men, taunting their cowardice and denting their morale, our legions draw ever nearer.'

'We will still have to fight alone for a while,' warned Oclatinius. 'But it gives us more of a chance to hold out.'

'This is Pandion,' said Macrinus, introducing a stocky young man dressed in a leather cuirass. 'He will be your chariot driver.'

'Augustus,' said Pandion, bowing low. 'It is an honour to serve you.'

Caracalla looked him up and down. 'Is he any good?'

'I'm told he is the best we have,' said Macrinus. 'He can turn the horses on a denarius, and has a bravery and a speed in a race that is unmatched by the most experienced charioteers in the Circus.'

Caracalla gave him a piercing glare. 'I have only one question for you, boy. Blue or Green?'

Pandion grinned. 'Blue, of course. Who would support anyone else?'

Caracalla smiled and clapped him on the shoulder. 'You'll do fine.' He looked at Oclatinius. 'Is it time?'

'Yes, Augustus, it's time.'

Caracalla marched out of his tent with Pandion close behind. An ornate chariot awaited him, a four-horse quadriga, held by an awed-looking slave. The horses standing abreast shuffled restlessly in their yokes, knowing that when they were carefully brushed clean, manes plaited, dressed in polished leather, something important was imminent.

Pandion mounted and took the reins from the slave, then held out a hand for Caracalla. Caracalla ignored the offer of help and bounded onto the back with an energetic leap.

'Lead us out,' he said.

Pandion flicked the reins, and with absolute precision, the four horses surged forward as one. The charioteer drove his Emperor out and turned him to face his troops, who were arrayed in battle formation. Caracalla surveyed them in silence for a moment, feeling a glow of pride. It was going to be a difficult day, he had no doubt of that, but he would not trade these soldiers for any others in history. Not Hannibal's, not Caesar's, not even Alexander's, however much he idolised the Macedonian conqueror. He genuinely loved these men, and knew they felt the same about him.

'Soldiers of Rome,' he said in a loud, deep voice that carried to the back of the assembled legion. 'Today will not be easy. The enemy have more men than us, and after our last victory, they will be fighting like wounded . animals. But we are Roman. Our courage, our strength, and our discipline will win out. Our brothers are marching to our aid, and will be here by the end of the day. We must hold until they arrive.

'I have faith in you. And I thank you for your faith in me. Most of you have fought with me before, in Britannia and elsewhere. I know you will not let me down. Together, we will conquer.' He thrust his sword into the air, and the soldiers let out a roar of approval that reverberated through his innards and filled him with elation.

'And to show the depth of my regard for you, I will offer my own person to the enemy, in single combat. Risk my life, and fight the barbarian chief for the honour of victory.'

Another great cheer, and despite Oclatinius' assurances that the Alamanni chief would not accept the offer of combat, he hoped otherwise. How glorious it would be to prove himself in front of his men. They would surely hail him as the new Alexander then.

He gave a final salute and tapped Pandion on the shoulder. Pandion wheeled the horses and rode out towards the enemy. The Alamanni were arrayed in a large group, about a quarter of a mile away from the Roman lines. They were in a wide valley, with steep hills to left and right. The trees on the slopes had been deforested, precluding ambush by either side. As he approached, the indistinct mass resolved into individual bodies, individual faces, many in their prime, but many too young or too old to be at war. He felt no guilt at the sight. They were the enemy, the other, and they must be destroyed, for the safety of Rome, and for his own glory.

When he was just out of bowshot, he ordered Pandion to halt. The charioteer swung the horses to the left and pulled them to a halt. From his platform on the chariot, he was able to call out so most of the Alamanni would be able to hear his words. He drew his sword and waved it in the air above his head as he spoke.

'People of the Alamanni. Your lives and lands are forfeit. Rome now owns them, as a man owns a slave or a dog. If you stand in our way, you will be destroyed utterly, as I destroyed the peoples of Caledonia. Your elders, your wives, your sons and daughters, will be put to the sword without mercy.

'But I give you one chance. Let your chief fight me, here and now, in single combat to the death. If your chief is victorious, I give you my word that my legions will leave this place and go back beyond the Rhenus, leaving you in peace. But if I am victorious, you will throw down your weapons and willingly surrender your lands and your persons into Roman ownership.

'What say you? Chlodulf. Where are you? Will you fight me, or will you cower behind your men like a frightened mouse?'

When his words finished silence hung over the valley. He ordered Pandion to ride up and down, parallel to the barbarian warriors, and as the charioteer controlled the horses in a perfect display of horsemanship, Caracalla repeatedly called out his challenge. 'Chlodulf! Fight me, you coward.'

There was a commotion behind the front line of inter-locked shields, raised voices and shouted arguments. Then the line parted, and a man rode out on a tall, grey mare. Caracalla saw the family resemblance to Chnodomar. But Chnodomar, though past his prime, still had some strength about him. This man had a rim of long hair around his bald pate, a wizened face, and was hunched

287

over. He rode stiffly, uncomfortably. But he held a spear in one hand.

Caracalla almost laughed aloud. O Serapis, please let him fight me.

'Chlodulf, I presume,' said Caracalla when the elderly chief was a dozen yards away.

'Emperor Antoninus,' said Chlodulf in a croaky voice, the Germanic accent heavy. 'Your name will forever be cursed, by the Alamanni and by all the peoples of the world, for your betrayal and dishonour.'

'Dishonour?' scoffed Caracalla. 'See me here, ready to fight you for honour and glory. Will you accept, or will you be the one to go to your gods in shame?'

'There is no honour in combat with one such as you. I simply ask you to leave our lands. We will destroy you if we have to. Despite your treachery, there are still many more of us than you. But we have no desire to shed more blood. Depart, and do not come back. We will not pursue you into your Empire.'

Now Caracalla did laugh, low and mocking. 'What an offer, to permit us to leave with our tails between our legs, like beaten curs, without a javelin being thrown. Simply tell me, will you fight me, or will you allow all your men to witness your shame?'

'There is no shame in refusing to treat a deceiver and backstabber as an equal. I decline your challenge, and when you are kneeling at my feet at the end of this day, you will have cause to regret your words and actions.'

With that, Chlodulf turned and rode back to his men, who parted in silence to let him through.

Caracalla felt an acute pang of disappointment. It was as Oclatinius had said. Of course. Oclatinius was always right. Still, Caracalla had hoped it would be different, that he would clash swords and shields, and take the head of the enemy chief.

He tapped Pandion on the shoulder, intending to head back to the Roman lines. Then he remembered the main reason he had ridden out here to challenge Chlodulf in the first place. He was supposed to be delaying the start of the battle. He ordered Pandion to drive up and down before the Alamanni. He taunted them as he passed, telling them they were led by a coward, that they would die in battle without honour, with the contempt of their gods.

Some of the Alamanni called back, shouted curses. But some could not meet his eye, turned away, looked at the ground or their comrades.

Eventually, Chlodulf or someone else in the Alamanni command must have tired of the display. As he returned back to the centre, their line suddenly split apart. Three riders charged out at breakneck pace, their heads down, each holding a spear, ready to throw.

Caracalla's heart skipped a beat and he cursed his complacency. Of course they would respond. He shouldn't have stayed so close.

But Pandion had been ready, and reacted instantly. He spun the horses back towards the Roman lines, flicked the reins, and threw the horses into a full gallop. Caracalla had to hang on tight as the chariot lurched, cornering on two wheels, before settling back down with a heavy thump. It took all his considerable strength to hold himself in the chariot with one hand while keeping his grip on his sword with the other.

But despite Pandion's quick reactions, the pursuing riders had already got up speed, and they were unencumbered by the chariot. They quickly gained on Caracalla, and when the first was ten yards behind, he drew back his arm and hurled his spear. Caracalla watched it come, headed straight and true for his chest.

Pandion flicked his reins, the horses leapt sideways, the chariot jinked, and the spear flew harmlessly past Caracalla's left side. Caracalla laughed aloud in exhilaration. This was living!

The second rider came closer. Caracalla looked down. There was a spear in the front of the chariot, and he picked it up, hefted it to assess its weight, then gripped it firmly two-thirds of the way down the shaft. The second rider drew back his spear and threw at exactly the same time as Caracalla. Again Pandion made a swift evasive turn, and Caracalla tumbled against the side of the chariot. The spear flew past the back of his shoulders, close enough that he could feel the wind it created.

He looked around to see the effects of his throw. The second rider was lying some distance behind now, flat on his back with the spear in his chest, while his horse carried on its headlong charge, directionless. The first rider, holding an axe in one hand now, closed with them. Caracalla wished he had another spear, and clutched his sword, preparing to fight.

He knew the Alamanni had a reputation as skilled horsemen, but he was still impressed when the rider positioned himself with two feet on the saddle in a low crouch, perfectly balanced. When he was close enough, the young warrior leapt across the gap between the horse and the chariot, swinging his axe down as he descended.

Caracalla caught the axe across the shaft with his sword and diverted the blow. The head crunched into the chariot, sending splinters of wood flying. Both weapons momentarily out of action, the warrior shoved Caracalla hard with his shoulder. Caracalla rocked back against the far edge of the chariot, felt himself falling backwards. He flailed, and his sword flew free and disappeared over the side. He realised that falling could mean the end of him. Out here between the armies, unmounted, the Alamanni riders could finish him off with spears and arrows before his own men could reach him. From the corner of his eye, he saw the ground rushing past, alarmingly close.

Pandion reached out with one hand, the other still steering the horses. He grabbed a strap on Caracalla's cuirass and pulled hard, yanking him back into the chariot. The warrior was instantly on him again, trying to bring his axe to bear. Caracalla grabbed his wrist with both hands, squeezed hard.

The Alamanni, like all Germans, were generally bulky and tall. But this young rider was lean and lithe, his lesser weight giving him greater manoeuvrability on horseback. Caracalla, by contrast, was short and muscular. When he had regained his balance, when it was hand to hand, strong arm against strong arm, it rapidly became no contest. Caracalla slammed the warrior's forearm against the edge of the chariot, snapping it like a dry twig. He cried out and his hand went limp, the axe falling to the ground. Caracalla butted him hard in the centre of the face, and as the warrior reeled back against the front of the chariot, Caracalla put a hand between his legs and lifted him bodily over the edge. He fell with a cry that was cut off abruptly as his body was crushed by the wheels. Caracalla felt the jolting impact, and once more had to hang on as the chariot bucked.

That motion saved his life. The spear from the third rider had been heading straight for him. When the chariot tipped sideways as it ran over the unfortunate warrior, the spear that would have taken him in the back instead passed under his armpit.

It hit Pandion in his right shoulder, and the charioteer slumped forward with a cry, dragging the reins to the left as his right arm went limp. The horses swung left, and the chariot tipped violently to the right. Caracalla was hurled over the side.

He reached out with one hand and gripped the edge of the chariot. His legs trailed in the dirt as the chariot threatened to topple over entirely.

Pandion yanked the reins to the right with his good arm, and the chariot righted itself. Caracalla grabbed hold with his other hand, and hauled himself back inside, panting heavily. He turned back to see the last rider had pulled up, and when he looked around he saw that he was nearly back to the safety of his own lines. Half a dozen cavalry had raced out to meet him.

He gently took the reins from Pandion and eased to the floor of the chariot, then guided the horses to a halt in front of his men. The Roman soldiers, who had witnessed the whole drama, erupted into cheers of adulation, and they chanted his name. He gave them a wave of acknowledgement, then directed the cavalry to take care of Pandion.

Behind him, the Alamanni began their advance.

-

Silus sat on horseback on the crest of the hill that overshadowed the left wing of the Roman army. Horses were not his preferred mode of transport, but then neither was boat, chariot or donkey cart. He only really trusted his own two feet. But as a scout, whose job it was to give the legions early warning of a surprise enemy attack on the flank, he accepted that he needed to be able to get away from enemy riders and get back to his own side as quickly as possible. And that meant riding.

He wiggled his backside uncomfortably in the saddle, and the horse sensed his unease and shifted nervously from foot to foot. He looked down at the valley that was soon to become a battlefield. A peaceful-looking place, with gentle undulations and a stream in the centre. It seemed incongruous that it would soon be filled with the cries of dying men, the stream running red.

The Roman forces were drawn up into a hollow square. In the centre of the square was the baggage and artillery, the sick and wounded, as well as the artillery – a couple of small ballistae and bolt-throwing scorpions – and the reserves. Light auxiliaries armed with slings and bows screened the front line of legionaries, and before them, and to the flanks and rear, was a thin layer of light cavalry. The formation was like a mobile marching camp, the important, vulnerable elements of the legion protected in the centre by a tough outer fence.

By contrast the Alamanni had no real structure. Just line after line of angry barbarians, eager to charge into the fray. From his knowledge of the relative strengths and fighting abilities of the two sides, he couldn't call the result one way or another. The Romans would fight smarter, but there were so many of the Germans.

He kept an eye on his surroundings, alert for the approach of any forces or enemy scouts, but was able to watch the events playing out below him. He watched the bizarre scene of Caracalla in his chariot, parading around in front of the Germans. Barely breathing, he watched Caracalla chased back to his own lines, the struggle in the chariot, the wounding of his charioteer, his narrow escape.

Then he watched the Alamanni begin their advance, and he felt like weeping. He strained his eyes, trying to see if any of the Alamanni was Odo, but he knew there was no hope, they were way too far away for him to make out any individual faces. He just hoped that Odo was safe at home, maybe recovering from a chest brought on by his plunge into the cold river.

The Roman front lines harried the advancing Germans. First the light cavalry hurled javelins, then retreated. Then the auxiliaries loosed a volley of arrows and bullets from their slings. Alamanni fell, some screaming and clutching wounds, others still, dead before they had swung an axe or sword in anger.

But the casualties were few, and when the Alamanni were within a score of yards, they burst into a charge with a roar that echoed around the valley. Silus could make out Atius no better than he could have seen Odo, but he imagined him there in the front line, and he hoped that his Christos was looking out for him.

Then, with a noise that was made of the dull thump of German bodies against Roman shields, mixed with the clash of weapons and the battle cries of the belligerents, the Alamanni crashed into the Roman front line.

Chapter Seventeen

It seemed like an age since Atius had last stood in a battle line. Not since his time in Britannia had he waited, shoulder to shoulder with legionaries on either side. Technically, Atius was not a legionary, having been promoted via the auxiliaries, but the men to his left and right seemed more than happy for an Arcanus with the rank of centurion to be fighting alongside them. Even if there was something a little wild in his eyes.

They rested their spears on the top of their shields, ready for the order to throw, after which they would draw their gladii and brace for the impact of the charging warriors. He could see them now, racing forward, the Roman cavalry and missile auxiliaries scattering before them. The artillery had stopped firing, as the Germans came too close to be sure the bolts and stones wouldn't hit their own men. A sudden panic gripped Atius, taking him by surprise. His heart started to race, his skin became clammy and cold, and his bowels attempted to loosen. He had to squeeze his buttocks to stop from soiling himself.

He had thought himself immune to the fear. After all he had been through, the danger, the killings, the captivity, the torture, it had almost been a relief to return to the familiarity of a legion. An impregnable mass of muscle, shield and armour, edge and point. What a fool he was. Imminent battle scared even the most hardened warriors. It was some small comfort to know that everyone around him was feeling exactly the same.

For a moment he felt like he was standing apart from himself, looking down from above on his own body. So small, insignificant, among the huge mass of Roman and German infantry. So fragile. He inspected himself, like a philosopher examining an interesting insect on the tip of his finger. His detachment felt emotional as well as physical. From this distance, it felt like none of it really mattered. Not victory. Not even his survival.

'Spears ready!'

The centurion's command snapped Atius out of it. Back into his body, with all the churning terror and excitement. He hefted his weapon, drew his arm back. He gripped so tight the shaft vibrated and the tip shook like a leaf in a stiff breeze. He could hear the thunder of German feet now, as the charge approached. Their battle cries became clear, the general swell of noise resolving into individual shouts, challenges and curses. He gritted his teeth. Had something happened to the centurion? They were getting too close. Why wasn't he giving the order?

'Throw!'

As one, the legionaries hurled their spears. They arced up, and back down into the onrushing barbarians. Many in the front rank checked their charge, ducked, weaved. Some fended the spears off with their shields, then had to discard their shields, weighted down with the missiles so they became a useless encumbrance. A few fell, stuck through in more or less vital parts of their bodies.

It wasn't nearly enough to make a difference.

The first Germans smashed into the Roman shields. Atius felt the impact like he had been hit by a charging bull. The only reason he wasn't knocked flat on his back was the legionaries behind him, bracing him. But of course that meant he was squashed from both front and back, and all the breath whooshed from him.

As he struggled to get air into his winded, compressed chest, the braced legionaries were forced back one step, two. Then the men of the second and third lines dug their heels in, pushed back, and the front stabilised. More Alamanni ploughed into the back of their own compatriots and the battle degenerated into a shoving match. Those in the fore found themselves crushed between their own men and the enemy, gasping like beached fish, while they fended off attacks with sword, axe and spear, at the same time stabbing forward over and between their shields.

The thrill of battle banished Atius' fear, and he thrust, twisted, withdrew, over and over. He felt, rather than saw, the blade strike home, find resistance, sometimes soft flesh, sometimes hard bone, and the accompanying screams gave him a warm sense of satisfaction. He imagined his opponent was Wigbrand the Chatti chief, or Romilda the priestess, even though these were not Chatti, and the priestess was already dead. The thought gave strength to his arm, and he fought with a fury that had his comrades casting sidelong glances at him, making sure to stay out of his reach in case they became accidental casualties.

But the energy that comes from battle lust can only take one so far. Quicker than he expected, he began to fatigue. He was nowhere near back to his full strength after the deprivation, maltreatment and inactivity of his captivity. And soon it told.

An axe came over the top of the shield, descending towards him. He swept his gladius upwards, but his counter was too weak. The axe deviated slightly from its path, so instead of cleaving his head in two, it glanced off the edge of his helmet. Still the blow was enough to stun him. He fell heavily onto his backside, then felt strong hands drag him unceremoniously back. He was dimly aware of someone stepping over him to take his place in the line, then the world, suddenly dotted with flashing lights, began to spin around him, and he collapsed backwards.

Silus watched the battle in frustration and anxiety. Part of him, maybe the larger part, felt he should be down there, standing shoulder to shoulder with Atius, the two friends protecting each other while they fought for Rome. All those other men too, putting their lives on the line for Emperor and Empire, while he sat on horseback, watching it all unfold like a gladiatorial fight, or a play at the theatre.

But the other part of him felt sympathy for the Alamanni, who were clearly the wronged people. Even from this distance, their righteous anger was palpable, and the fury with which they fought underlined the fact that they were struggling for their very existence.

Silus winced as the front lines crashed into each other, and found that he had been clenching his fist so hard as he watched the first few moments play out that his fingernails had dug half-moons into his palm. He consciously willed his hand to relax, then looked around him. No sign of an enemy flanking force. They had obviously decided to keep it simple. Use their superior numbers to overwhelm the Romans. Slaughter them as rapidly as possible, before reinforcements could arrive. They must be aware that this wasn't the full extent of the Roman forces in Germania, but they also knew that the Emperor was with this army. It took no great strategist to know that if you cut off the head of the snake its body was no longer a threat. Even Caledonia had been saved from complete destruction by the death of Severus, leaving his sons to race back to Rome to consolidate their power.

He looked back to the fight, then a movement in the corner of his field of vision caught his attention. A rider. Coming towards him along the hillside from the German side. Solitary. So a scout, like him, he supposed. He put his hand on the hilt of his gladius and waited for the man to approach. As the figure drew nearer, he saw that man barely fit the description. A slender individual, little more than a boy. Just like…

Oh no.

But of course. It was no coincidence. He should have been prepared for this. Odo was a scout, just like Silus. That was why he had been chosen to help Silus rescue Atius in the first place. It was only natural that he would be sent here, up the hillside to warn against surprise flank attacks from the Romans. That neither side had planned such a stratagem meant that Silus and Odo now sat on horseback, half a dozen yards apart, looking at each other with eyes full of sadness.

For a long while, neither spoke. Then Silus, said, 'Ride away.'

Odo shook his head.

'Turn around,' said Silus. His voice was pleading. 'Go. Tell your superiors that there was nothing to see.'

'I'm not going to do that, Silus,' said Odo. His voice was so flat, so distant. So unlike the cheerful companion whose company and hospitality Silus had enjoyed so recently.

'Please. This will only end one way.'

'I could have saved him. My father.'

'It was hopeless. You would have died alongside him.'

'You denied me that chance. You lied to me, tricked me.'

'To save you!' Silus was exasperated. 'Please believe me, I only found out when it was too late to stop it. I could do only one thing. Make sure you lived.'

'At what cost?'

Odo slowly dismounted, and drew his sword, a short Roman gladius, maybe given to him when in service to Rome, maybe looted from a dead legionary. Silus hesitated, then swung down from his own horse.

'I can't fight you. Not after everything,' said Silus.

'I'm not giving you the choice. Look down there.'

Silus glanced down at the battle. The Romans were sorely pressed, giving ground as wave upon wave of Alamanni fell upon them. The Roman reserves were being thrown into the gaps in their defensive line as men fell. Maybe Atius was one of those fallen. Maybe he was dead already. After all they had been through together, wouldn't Silus feel something if Atius had died?

'I'm not naive. If we lose this battle, the Alamanni are finished, for a generation or more. But if we win, if we defeat your Emperor, even kill him, then the retribution of Rome will be as bad, if not worse. There is no hope for us now. What have I to live for?'

'There is so much...' began Silus.

'No.' The single word was like a descending axe, cutting the sentence short. 'But I can die with honour. Defend yourself, Silus.' He stepped forward.

Still Silus did not draw his sword. Odo hesitated, clearly unwilling to cut down an unarmed man. Emotions warred in his eyes. Then he let out a howl of anguish and despair and swung his gladius two-handed at Silus' neck.

Instinct took over then. Whether a rational Silus, given time to think, would have accepted the blow, rather than be forced to fight back and kill his friend, he would never know. Because the animal was at the fore now, the predator, the prey. Kill or be killed.

He ducked under the blow, rolled across the damp, grassy earth and came back to his feet with his sword already in his hands. Odo pressed forward, swinging left to right, right to left. Silus dodged, parried, ducked again. Still he retained enough control, his human mind ruling the animal just enough to stop him striking back. Maybe he could disarm Odo, force him to surrender.

But Odo had given himself to a battle fury that Silus had never seen before in the youth. He howled and spat and cursed as he hacked and slashed. And then the moment came, when Odo over-extended his reach, lost his balance.

The animal Silus struck. Before he even knew it had happened, he thrust his sword into Odo's abdomen, twisted, pulled. A gout of blood came out with the blade, and Odo fell to his knees, dropping his sword, mouth open in shock and pain.

Silus was instantly by his side, his own sword discarded. As Odo tumbled backwards, he caught him, cradled him in his arms.

Odo looked up at him, spittle on his chin, tears trickling out of the corners of his eyes.

'Oh. Silus, it hurts.'

Silus looked down at the lad, his own tears flowing freely now.

'I'm so sorry.'

'It's not your fault,' said Odo. 'The gods willed we should be enemies. You know...' He coughed, and red-brown blood spewed out of his mouth. Silus wiped his face clean with the sleeve of his tunic, and Odo breathed heavily for a few moments, before summoning up the strength to speak again.

'You know, I would have been proud to call you brother.'

Silus frowned. The comment seemed incongruous.

'And I know you would have made my sister happy.'

Comprehension rolled over him. Oh.

'You knew?'

Odo tried to laugh, coughed again. More blood. When he was able to speak again, his voice was noticeably weaker, and all colour had left his skin, his boyish red pimples vivid against the pallor of his face.

'I told you. I'm young, but I'm not naive. I saw the way you looked at each other. But now, I think my sister would find it hard to love the man who killed her brother.'

Silus thought of his strange love-hate paternal relationship with Tituria, whose family he had murdered. He thought of Caracalla's relationship with his stepmother, whose son, his half-brother, the Emperor had killed. And he felt suddenly so exhausted. Odo was right. Ima would not love him. But nor would he put himself through the pain of loving her. Not with Odo's eyes staring out of hers accusingly, every time he looked at her.

'Odo. I would have been proud to call you brother, too.'

Odo nodded and closed his eyes. Silus stayed with him, holding him, as his breathing became deeper, more irregular. He didn't know at what point the boy lost consciousness, but he knew, when the breathing stopped, the body stiffened, the point at which he died. He hugged the young Alamanni against him, and he shook as he wept.

Below him, the battle raged on.

–

Atius lay in a damp puddle. The earth rocked like he was on a boat in a rough storm, and he put a hand down to try to steady himself. The puddle was strangely warm and sticky, and when he lifted his palm to his face he saw it was covered in congealed blood. He thought, with a strange sense of detachment, that the blood must be his, until he turned his face sideways and found himself looking at a headless corpse, still oozing from the severed vessels.

The shock made him sit up, and though his head spun, he did not pass out again. Though he had been dragged back from the front of the battle when he was struck, the front line had retreated back to him, and he was in danger of being trampled by the hobnailed boots of his own side as they took step after step in reverse.

He shuffled backwards on his seat, then cautiously levered himself upwards. He had lost his sword and shield, but the decapitated soldier beside him still clutched a gladius and his shield lay nearby. Atius pried the surprisingly strong grip off the hilt and swung the sword experimentally twice, to test its weight. A gap opened in the lines a couple of feet in front of him as a legionary toppled sideways when an axe bit into the angle between neck and shoulder.

Atius grabbed the discarded shield and stepped into the lacuna. A spear thrust over the top of his shield nearly went through his forehead, but Silus was able to sway to his left just enough for the tip to pass harmlessly past his right ear. He thrust his gladius through the tiny gap between his shield and his neighbour's and was rewarded with a soft resistance, and a low gasp of pain. He shoved forward with his shield, the boss crunching into something bony, and his attacker fell away.

Another appeared instantly in his place, and Atius shoved with his shield again. This one was armed with a stabbing sword, and he used the Roman tactic of thrusting through gaps, rather than swinging, clubbing and bludgeoning, which was less effective in the closely packed ranks. Atius had to gyrate his body to avoid a blade in his guts, and his own counter-thrust was ineffective. The Alamanni warrior snarled at him, cursed him in his guttural language as he stabbed again, and this time the attack found Atius' midriff, even as he twisted away.

Fortunately, Atius' desperate evasion attempt changed the angle of attack just enough that his armour deflected the blow. The armour parted around the sharp iron, and the edge sliced his skin, but the point did not find its target, his soft innards.

But Atius was off balance now, and slow from the head injury and his general poor state of fitness. The warrior withdrew his sword and prepared for a thrust to Atius' face over the top of the shield, and though Atius brought his own blade up to counter, he knew he was going to be too slow.

The legionary to Atius' right saw the threat, and stabbed hard in the direction of Atius' opponent. The gladius tip went into the soft temple, and the barbarian's eyes rolled up into his head as he died instantly.

Atius turned to thank his comrade, only to see a spear skewer his neck from front to back. The legionary sank to his knees, clutching at the spear and yanking it from his killer's hands. Atius stabbed out, and his neighbour's assailant staggered back.

For a moment, Atius found himself unopposed in the line, and he was able to take stock. All the Roman reserves had been thrown forward down, to shore up holes in the defences, or reinforce parts of the line where the defenders were looking shaky. Even Caracalla was in the action with his Praetorians, some way down the line from Atius. He had charged into a breakthrough on the left, his Praetorian cavalry with him, and thrown back the attackers forcefully. Now he was swinging around him with a long spatha, hacking down any who came near.

It was obvious from his luxurious and highly polished attire that he was important, and it didn't take much guesswork to conclude this was the Emperor. Consequently, the Alamanni leaders directed their reserves in his direction, hoping to bring the battle to a swift conclusion. But the Praetorian cavalry and the Emperor's bodyguard fought like lions. Arrows arced towards him but were swatted away by his companions' shields. Spears thrust out but were knocked aside or cut in two with sharp blades. Axes were swung or hurled, but their wielders were cut down.

Caracalla made no headway into the mass of warriors, but his mere presence drew swarms of Alamanni towards him like wasps attacking honeycakes, and that alone relieved the pressure elsewhere. But even that was not enough. The Alamanni were just too many. And with the reserves used, when defender was cut down, there was no one to step up to plug the leak. At first a trickle, and then like a dam breaking, the Alamanni burst through. Now the defending legionaries were beset not just from the front, but from behind as well.

The structured formation of the Romans broke down, and suddenly it was every man for himself. Atius found himself back to back with another legionary, fighting for their lives. Exultant Alamanni swarmed around them, crying out in victory, waving their weapons in the air as some made for the baggage carts to begin looting, while others, the more disciplined, pressed their advantage home.

For the Romans were not yet done. Though they no longer fought in the protection of their close-packed ranks, they still had months and years of training. They had strength and stamina, their swords were like extensions of their arms, and now, as the Alamanni had been at the start of battle, they were fighting for their very survival. They expected no mercy from these people whose unarmed kin they had so recently slaughtered.

So the fighting continued, with no let-up. In the end it came down to stubbornness. Atius was not willing to give up, not ready to die, not after he had stayed alive against all the odds so far. Though he could barely lift his sword, though his shield sagged, though his comrade behind him stiffened, gurgled, died, Atius fought on.

And when he finally felt the end nearing, the last reserves of his energy gone, he heard the sound of bucinators blaring their sweet trumpet notes across the valley. He was unable to turn to see the source of the noise, but it was unmistakable, and if he had had any doubts, the thunder of horse hooves dispelled them immediately.

The Alamanni heard the sound too, stepped back from the fight, turned their heads in fear.

Now Atius could look, and his heart lifted at the sight of a wedge of a hundred heavily armoured Roman auxiliary cavalry charging down the hillside to take the Alamanni in the rear. Behind them, preparing their charge as soon as the cavalry had struck and retreated, were the infantry, three legions, a little fatigued from the forced march, but fresher than any man on either side on that battlefield.

Half the Alamanni were skirmishing against pockets of resistance while the others raided the meat and beer wagons and looted the dead. The cream of their leadership dead in the massacre, the remaining nobles and chiefs had no control over their men, and when the cavalry struck, there was no defence.

The Alamanni scattered in panic, but the Romans were quickly on them. Those that were outright fleeing were easy fodder for the short lances and long spathas of the cavalry, who speared them like fish in a pond. Those that stood and fought faced the full force of the legionaries.

It was no contest. Barbarian disorganisation and fatigue fought Roman energy and discipline. All Alamanni resistance disintegrated, and then the slaughter began, no less bloody or complete than the previous massacre, for all that these barbarians were armed and prepared for a fight.

Atius' attackers melted away, and with disconcerting abruptness he found himself all but alone. Around him lay a circle of dead and dying, Roman and German. The focus of the battle rolled off into the distance, like a thunderstorm passing from overhead to somewhere far away. His hands dropped to his sides, the last of his strength deserting him with the fading of the danger. His shield and sword dropped from numb fingers. Though they crashed to the ground, he didn't hear them.

A sudden thought occurred to him. He looked up towards the hill crest, where Silus had been stationed. He could see two figures there, one kneeling, one lying, but he could make out no more than that. He feared for Silus, but as he looked around him at the battlefield strewn with dead and dying, he could summon no emotion. He tried to pray, but even that was beyond him. Was this his retribution? Was he healed? Sated?

He sat down heavily, hugged his knees to his chest, and rocked back and forth, trembling violently.

Epilogue

Odo's body was so light, Silus' stout horse seemed not to notice the extra burden. The steed plodded slowly through the countryside of Germania Magna, and Silus let it choose its own pace, which turned out to be appropriately funereal. The roads were full of refugees, mainly women, children and old men, some dressed in fine, Roman-style robes, others in little more than rags, all mingled together as they fled east. Some rode in farm carts laden with furniture, tools, cooking utensils, pulled by oxen. A few were on horseback, trotting past the rest, their gazes steadfastly forward as they tried to ignore the envious and pleading glares of those they were overtaking. The majority were on foot, taking with them whatever they could bear on their backs.

A small child, a girl of around the age his daughter had been when she died, stared at Odo as he passed her, then looked up. She had a snotty nose and muddy cheeks, and she carried a doll in the crook of her elbow, the thumb of the same arm firmly lodged in her mouth. Silus silently wished her a speedy journey to safety. He hoped the other German tribes would accommodate their uprooted cousins. There were no guarantees. The Germans were as likely to fight each other as the Romans. Maybe these people were just marching to a different type of slavery, working in fields and serving noble chiefs, rather than labouring in mines or being at the beck and call of Roman matrons in sumptuous villas.

It wasn't his fault. He didn't do it, he couldn't stop it. No matter how many times he told himself this, he couldn't escape the aching guilt. Even when he tried to fix his eyes away from the wretched, defeated people, Odo was always in his line of sight, limply accusing. Someone else he cared about, who was now dead. The list was becoming longer. Velua and Sergia, his wife and daughter. Daya, his fellow Aracanus. Now Odo. Maybe it was dangerous to be cared for by Silus. Maybe he should stop caring.

His thoughts drifted to the strange young son of Marcellus and Julia Soaemia. Avitus. He had saved that boy. He wondered where he was now. Was he with his father in Numidia still? Was he with his crazy mother? Silus felt a sudden surge of protectiveness towards him.

Eventually he came to the fork that led to Odo's family home. Ran and Modi spotted him from some distance and they raced out to meet him, barking excitedly. But when they reached the horse, they came to Odo and sniffed his dangling fingers. Their excitement vanished. They surely couldn't understand, but still they trotted slowly alongside Silus' horse, head and tails held low, flanking him like an honour guard.

Ada and Ima were waiting for him at the door. Ada's face was hard, expressionless. Ima was not so emotionless, and rushed over to Odo, clutching at him and weeping in choking gasps. Silus dismounted, and gently detached Ima. Then he lifted Odo into his arms, and stood before Ada.

She regarded her son for a long moment. Then she gestured for Silus to enter the house. He carried the body inside, and laid it on a couch. He tried to arrange the limbs in a peaceful position, but Ada shooed him away, and took over the task herself, crossing the hands on his chest, straightening his legs, taking a damp cloth to bathe his face.

Then the facade of stoicism split open, and she collapsed on the body of her son, hugging him tight, her body racked by loud sobs. Ima came to her and knelt beside her, one arm on her mother and one on her dead brother, and joined in the wails.

Silus stood back, shifting uncomfortably from foot to foot, not sure where to look. He wondered if he should just leave, his last duty to Odo finished. But at that moment, Ada stood, straightened her clothing, wiped her eyes and turned to face him.

'You must be tired from your ride, please sit. Ima. Ima!' Ima reluctantly let go of Odo and looked at her mother. 'Go and fetch Silus some beer and some meat.'

Ima flashed him a look of hatred, but did as her mother bade. Silus found a padded stool to sit on, and Ada sat on a couch opposite him. She regarded him steadily until Ima returned. Silus hadn't realised how thirsty and hungry he was until he was presented with the food and drink, and he accepted it gratefully.

'He died well?' asked Ada abruptly. Silus had a mouthful of venison, and had to chew fast and swallow so he could speak.

'He did. Like a true German warrior.'

'It was you that killed him.'

Silus flushed, but he wouldn't lie. He nodded. 'The gods put us on opposite sides of this war.'

'Not the gods. Your Emperor started this.'

Silus couldn't disagree, and he felt a surge of anger towards Caracalla. He had fought for that man, risked his life, killed for him. He felt dirty, that the Emperor that he followed so dutifully could have behaved like this.

'How is Ewald?'

'Recovering. He will not see you.'

Silus nodded. 'I understand.'

'And my husband?' asked Ada, voice flat and hopeless.

Silus looked down. 'I couldn't save him,' he said quietly.

Suddenly Ima flew at him. Crying incoherently, she struck him around the head and arms with her closed fists. He bowed his head and took the blows, unflinching. His cheekbone bruised and his lip split and he made no move to stop her. Eventually the storm blew out, and she stepped back and turned away, throwing herself once more over Odo and holding him tight.

'Soldiers are coming,' said Silus. 'They will show no mercy. You need to leave here. Take what you can carry and get far away.'

Ada glanced involuntarily to the open front door, and he saw a chill run through her. Then she straightened her back and looked at Silus.

'I think there is no more to say, is there,' she said.

Silus stroked Ran or Modi, he wasn't sure which of the dogs had been sitting by his side since he arrived, playing the companion or guard. He took a last look at Ida and Odo. Then he walked out, mounted his horse, and rode west.

He travelled past more streams of refugees, who looked at him in envy at his steed and surprise at his direction.

What direction was that? He had no real idea. He hadn't reported back to Oclatinius since the battle, but really, fuck him. He still wanted to confront Caracalla, but he had calmed enough to know that was suicidal. He would go back to Lipari, to see Tituria, at some point. But what about Avitus? He would love to know how the fascinating child was getting on. Maybe he would find him, and see how he was. Or would that bring down disaster on the boy who wanted his own Empire? Silus didn't know. He didn't know much any more. But he had a feeling, a knot in his gut, a nagging at the back of his head. Anxiety, danger. Was it just a part of his life now? Or was there something really looming? Something that fate and the gods had saved up, just to make his life even more miserable?

But the thought of seeing Avitus kindled a small spark inside him. It wasn't much amongst all this darkness, but it gave him hope that maybe there was light to come. He gritted his teeth, set his eyes straight ahead, and rode on.

–

Oclatinius and Festus surveyed the battlefield from a distance. They had not been present for the battle itself. They were both old, and would have been more hindrance than help in the sort of struggle that had taken place today. Only now, with the job of the carrion feeders – human and animal – well under way, did they arrive.

It was a familiar sight to them both, and though it took a strange type of person to be completely inured to the grisly vista, it did not affect them overly.

'It all worked out, then,' said Festus.

'So it seems,' said Oclatinius. They sat astride comfortable, placid mounts. Old warhorses, whose job now lay away from the battle, in more sedentary occupations. But no less responsible, for that.

'I owe your man Silus,' said Festus. 'I don't know if Atius or Eustachys would have broken eventually, but if they had, we would be looking at a very different outcome today. At the best, the Alamanni would have never come to the peace conference, and we would have had to fight their whole forces. In the worst case, they would have come to the peace conference secretly armed, and turned the ambush on us.'

'Or we could have honoured our alliance,' interjected Oclatinius.

'You think they would have remained our allies after learning of our plans?'

Oclatinius looked out at the corpses. The majority were Alamanni. Although the Romans had taken heavy losses in the first part of the battle, once the reinforcements arrived, it had rapidly become a rout. Caracalla's plan to defeat the Alamanni confederation before turning on the Chatti and the more northerly tribes had succeeded beyond his expectations. But Oclatinius feared what price Rome would pay for the treachery in years to come.

'If only Eustachys had made it through to Erhard,' said Festus. 'With the information that Rome would soon annihilate the Alamanni, he could have fomented a rebellion among the Chatti and split their forces. Now, we have another formidable barbarian enemy to deal with.' He sighed and picked up his reins. 'We should find Caracalla.'

'Festus,' said Oclatinius, and his tone carried a warning. Festus looked at him sharply.

'I'm not blind,' said Oclatinius. 'And I know that you do not underestimate my intelligence, nor my network of informers.'

'What are you talking about?'

'Macrinus.'

'What about him?'

'I know his ambition. And I know yours.'

Festus said nothing, simply pursed his lips.

'I'm not going to Caracalla with what I know. But just be aware. My powers are not without limit. Despite our past, what you did for me, there are some things from which I just cannot protect you.'

'I don't need your protection,' snapped Festus.

'You needed my help very recently,' said Oclatinius, his voice even. 'Don't believe you are invincible. Even Achilles had his heel.'

Festus flicked the reins and cantered away.

Oclatinius shook his head and sighed. Then, more slowly, he followed.

Author's note

As with most of this period of history, the historical sources are scarce. As with all the books in this series, much of my material comes from the only full-length text about Caracalla, by Ilkka Syvänne (see bibliography). I have included the relevant texts from Herodian and Cassius Dio that comprise much of what we know about Caracalla's German campaign, but as discussed in my previous author's notes (and in the novels themselves, since Cassius Dio was Caracalla's contemporary), these historians were considerably biased against Caracalla. Many Roman emperors have been demonised despite doing no worse than others who are regarded as 'Great'.

Caracalla's betrayal of the Alamanni is a case in point. Cassius Dio clearly disapproves. Syvänne, in an effort to give the other side of the story, portrays it as a brilliant tactic to eliminate a serious threat to the Empire. The rights and wrongs of this are very much in the eye of the beholder, and it likely divided even contemporary Roman opinion.

There is little contemporary detail on Caracalla's campaign against the Germans, but Syvänne has speculated on the most likely possibilities. I have used these, while accepting that they are only speculation, and so have felt at liberty to speculate myself, and change some details from Dr Syvänne's narrative.

Caracalla's encounter with the Alamanni is the first mention in the contemporary historical literature of this important tribe, who gave their name to Allemagne, the French name for Germany. The origin of the word Alamanni (or Alemanni) was probably from an old German word meaning 'all mankind', and the tribe probably grew out of the Suebi, who lived along the river Main. The Iuthungi and Lentienses also contributed to the Alamanni confederacy, and there may have even been Roman settlers who joined their ranks. Other tribes in the area at the time included the Chatti, who are probably the Cenni that Cassius Dio mentions, as well as the Chauci and Marcomanni. The Marcomanni were a much diminished force, however, after their defeat by Marcus Aurelius one hundred and fifty years earlier.

The Alamanni appeared to be a peaceful and romanised nation prior to Caracalla's surprise attack. It may be that they would have been good allies to Rome, and could even have changed history if they had remained on the Roman side as the Empire endured wave after wave of invasions from the east in subsequent centuries. But either Caracalla didn't trust them, or he saw their defeat as an easy way of obtaining victories to the benefit of his own reputation. Whatever his thinking, Caracalla removed the Alamanni as a threat to Rome for a generation, achieving his own objectives while storing up trouble in the shape of the bitter enmity of the tribe in the future.

The whirlwind was reaped in 256 AD when the Alamanni king, Chrocus, whose mother possibly lost family to Caracalla's campaign, descended on Gaul, burning, pillaging and slaughtering. They made it into Italy, and it was several years later that they were finally stopped by Lake Garda. And they continued to invade the Roman Empire periodically until finally they were defeated as allies of Attila the Hun. However, they only really stopped their centuries-long war with Rome when the Roman Empire had retreated far from their territory in the late fifth century, and they had to contend instead with the Franks, their eventual conquerors.

A note here on the use of historical language. Whether to use modern terms in historical fiction is a regular topic on writing fora, and as with just about any subject, opinion is divided. Some purists believe that you should avoid words that don't have their origins in the time period you are writing about. For example, I have seen it argued that you shouldn't use the title 'sir' for stories set in the classical world, since this word was first used in the middle ages as an honorific for a knight. Leaving aside that it derives from the vulgar Latin 'senior', if writers were confined to using words of Latin origin, that would limit us to just a portion of the richness of the English language.

There may be a better argument for being more cautious about the choice of words in dialogue. But this ignores the fact that we are writing in English, effectively translating the Latin into words understandable to a modern audience (albeit, in the case of fiction, words that were mostly never actually spoken in the first place). The author then has to juggle between giving his characters a voice that is authentic both to them as fictional individuals, and to the time period. Avoiding obviously modern colloquialisms is important. For example, the urban thesaurus gives us a rich lexicon to describe drunkenness (https://urbanthesaurus. org/synonyms/drunk) and synonyms such as gazebo'd, ham-sandwiched and routed by the liquid viking would sound jarringly uncontemporary. Conversely, I would contend that phrases such as shit-faced, pissed, hammered and arseholed can give the impression of earthy conversation without using non-contemporaneous imagery. Though I don't have any evidence that these words were used, even in their Latin forms, we have little information on how Latin was spoken among the masses, since most texts that survived were written in classical rather than vulgar Latin.

Of course some choice language has survived, which brings me to the use of profanity. Unfortunately, my book does contain some naughty words. There would be something ridiculously comical in sanitising the language of hardened soldiers and assassins who have lived through multiple traumas, reminiscent of the 'Far Side' cartoon in which a nerdy man in hell curses someone: 'Dash you to heck.' For those who think the Romans didn't swear and curse, I refer you to the graffiti of Pompeii ('Amplicatus, I know that Icarus is buggering you. Salvius wrote this', 'Theophilus, don't perform oral sex on girls against the city wall like a dog'), Petronius' Satyricon ('You whore of female passivity. Not even your breath is pure'), and the curse tablets of Bath ('may the worms, cancer, and maggots penetrate his hands, head, feet, as well as his limbs and marrows'). And I will leave you with Catullus, the love poet studied in schools, raging at his friends: 'pedicabo ego vos et irrumabo'.

Herodian on Caracalla

Adapted from Herodian's history of his own times, original transl. J. Hart 1749, book IV, chapter vii

After committing such crimes as these, hounded by his conscience and finding life in Rome intolerable, the emperor decided to leave the city to see to matters in the garrison camps and visit the provinces. Leaving Italy, he journeyed to the banks of the Danube, where he concerned himself with the northern part of his empire. At the same time he exercised by driving in chariot races and by fighting at close quarters with wild animals of every kind. Only occasionally did he sit as judge, although he was quick to grasp the essentials of a case in court and quick to pass judgment on the basis of the arguments presented.

He grew especially fond of the Germans in those regions. After gaining their friendship, he entered into alliances with them, and selected for his personal body-guard the strongest and most handsome young men. He frequently put off the Roman cloak and donned German dress, appearing in the short, silver-embroidered cloaks which they customarily wear, augmented by a yellow wig with the locks arranged in the German style.

Delighted with the emperor's antics, the barbarians became very fond of him, as did the Roman soldiers also, particularly because of his lavish gifts of money but also because he always played the soldier's part. If a ditch had to be dug anywhere, the emperor was the first man to dig; if it were necessary to bridge a stream or pile up a high rampart, it was the same; in every task involving labor of hand or body, the emperor was first man to the job.

He set a frugal table and even went so far as to use wooden dishes at his meals. He ate the bread that was available; grinding with his own hands his personal ration of grain, he made a loaf, baked it in the ashes, and ate it. Scorning luxuries, he used whatever was cheapest and issued to the poorest soldier. He pretended to be delighted when they called him fellow soldier instead of emperor. For the most part he marched with the troops, carrying his own arms and rarely using a chariot or a horse.

Occasionally he even placed the standards of the legions on his shoulders and bore them along; these standards, tall and decorated with many gold ornaments, were a heavy burden for even the strongest soldiers. For these actions Caracalla won the affection of the soldiers by his military prowess and gained their admiration by his feats of strength. And it is certainly true that the performance of such strenuous tasks by a man of small stature was worthy of admiration.

Dio Cassius on Caracalla

Adapted from an English translation of Dio's Roman History, Book 77, by Earnest Cary PhD, 1914, taken from the Lacus Curtius website.
https://penelope.uchicago.edu/Thayer/E/Roman/Texts/Cassius_Dio/78*.html

Epitome of Book LXXVIII xii–xv

Such was his character in general; I will now state what sort of person he was in war. Abgarus, king of the Osroëni, when he had once got control of the kindred tribes, visited upon their leaders all the worst forms of cruelty. Nominally he was compelling them to change to Roman customs, but in fact he was indulging his authority over them to the full. Antoninus tricked the king of the Osroëni, Abgarus, inducing him to visit him as a friend, and then arresting and imprisoning him; and so, Osroëne being thus left without a king, he subdued it.

When the king of the Armenians was quarrelling with his own sons, Antoninus summoned him in a friendly letter, pretending that he would make peace between them; but he treated them as he had treated Abgarus. The Armenians, however, instead of yielding to him, had recourse to arms, and no one thereafter would trust him in anything whatever. Thus he learned by experience how great the penalty is for an emperor when he practises deceit upon friends.

He likewise took the greatest credit to himself because, after the death of Vologaesus, king of the Parthians, the king's sons began to fight for the throne, thus pretending that a situation was due to chance had been brought about through his own contriving. So keen, it seems, was the delight he always took in the fact and in the dissensions of the brothers and in the mutual slaughter of persons in no way connected with himself.

But he did not hesitate to write to the senate regarding the Parthian rulers, who were brothers and at variance, that the brothers' quarrel would work great harm to the Parthian State, as if this sort of thing could destroy the barbarians and yet had saved Rome – whereas in fact Rome had been, one might say, utterly overthrown thereby! It was not that, to seal a crime that brought a great curse upon mankind, but that vast numbers of citizens had been falsely accused, not merely those who had sent letters to his brother or brought him gifts, either when he was still Caesar or when he had become emperor, but even the others who had never any dealings with him. Indeed, if anyone so much as wrote the name Geta or even uttered it, he was immediately put to death. Hence the poets no longer used it even in comedies; and in fact the possessions of all those in whose wills the name appeared were confiscated. Much that he did was done for the purpose of raising money.

He exhibited his hatred for his dead brother by abolishing the observance of his birthday, and he vented his anger upon the stones that had supported his statues, and melted down the coinage that displayed his features. And not content with even this, he now more than ever practised unholy rites, and would force others to share his pollution, by making a kind of annual offering to his brother's Manes.

Though feeling and acting thus with regard to his brother's murder, he took delight in the dissension of the barbarian brothers, on the ground that the Parthians would suffer some great harm because of it.

The Germanic nations, however, afforded him neither pleasure nor any specious claim to wisdom or courage, but proved him to be a downright cheat, a simpleton, and an arrant coward. Antoninus made a campaign against the Alamanni and whenever he saw a spot suitable for habitation, he would order, 'There let a fort be erected. There let a city be built.' And he gave these places names relating to himself, though the local designations were not changed; for some of the people were unaware of the new names and others supposed he was jesting. Consequently he came to feel contempt for these people and would not spare even them, but accorded treatment befitting the bitterest foes to the very people whom he claimed to have come to help. For he summoned their men of military age, pretending that they were to serve as mercenaries, and then at a given signal – by raising aloft his own shield

– he caused them all to be surrounded and cut down, and he sent horsemen round about and arrested all the others.

Antoninus sent a letter to the senate commending Pandion, a man who had formerly been an assistant of charioteers, but in the war against the Alamanni drove the emperor's chariot and thereby became both his comrade and fellow-soldier. In this letter he asserted that he had been saved by this man from an exceptional peril; and he was not ashamed at feeling more gratitude toward him than toward the soldiers, whom in their turn he always regarded as superior to us senators.

Some of the most distinguished men whom Antoninus slew he ordered to be cast out unburied. He made search for the tomb of Sulla and repaired it, and also reared a cenotaph to Mesomedes, who had made a compilation of citharoedic modes; he showed honour to the latter because he was himself learning to play the lyre, and to the former because he was emulating his cruelty.

On necessary and urgent campaigns, however, he was simple and frugal, taking his part scrupulously in the menial duties on terms of equality with the rest. Thus, he would march with the soldiers and run with them, neither bathing nor changing his clothing, but helping them in every task and choosing exactly the same food as they had; and he would often send to the enemy's leaders and challenge them to single combat. The duties of a commander, however, in which he ought to have been particularly well versed, he performed in a very unsatisfactory manner, as if he thought that victory lay in the performance of the humble duties mentioned rather than in good generalship.

He waged war also against the Cenni, a Germanic tribe. These warriors are said to have assailed the Romans with the utmost fierceness, even using their teeth to pull from their flesh the missiles with which the Osroëni wounded them, so that they might have their hands free for slaying their foes without interruption. Nevertheless, even they accepted a defeat in name in return for a large sum of money and allowed him to make his escape back into the province of Germany. Some of their women who were captured by the Romans, upon being asked by Antoninus whether they wished to be sold or slain, chose the latter fate; then, upon being sold, they all killed themselves and some slew their children as well.

Many also of the people living close to the ocean itself near the mouths of the Albis sent envoys to him asking for his friendship, though their real purpose was to get money. This was made clear by the fact that, when he had done as they desired, many attacked him, threatening to make war, and yet he came to terms with all of them. For even though the terms proposed were contrary to their wishes, yet when they saw the gold pieces they were captivated. The gold that he gave them was of course genuine, whereas the silver and the gold currency that he furnished to the Romans was debased; for he manufactured the one kind out of lead plated with silver and the other out of copper plated with gold.

He likewise published outright to the world some of his basest deeds, as if they were excellent and praiseworthy, whereas others he revealed unintentionally through the very precautions which he took to conceal them, as, for example, in the case of the money.

Antoninus devastated the whole land and the whole sea and left nothing anywhere unharmed.

Acknowledgements

Thank you to my family for supporting me through another novel, including my mother who has been reading this series against my advice, and consequently giving herself nightmares. Thanks to Michael and Kit at Canelo and Miranda Ward for a thorough copy-edit.

Bibliography and Further Reading

As usual, I have consulted too many texts in the research for this novel to list, but some of the principal books I have relied on are included here:

Bowman, A. K., Garnsey, P. & Cameron, A., (2005) *The Cambridge Ancient History: Volume XII, the Crisis of Empire AD 193–337*, 2nd edition, Cambridge University Press, Cambridge

Carroll, M., (2001) *Romans, Celts and Germans, the German Provinces of Rome*, Tempus, Stroud

Goldsworthy, A., (2011) *The Complete Roman Army*, Thames & Hudson, London

Grant, M., (1996) *The Severans, the Changed Roman Empire*, Routledge, Abingdon

La Baume, P., (Not known) *The Romans on the Rhine*, Stollfuss Verlag, Bonn

Mattingly, H., (1948) *Tacitus on Britain and Germany, a New Translation of the Agricola and the Germania*, Penguin, West Drayton

Matyszak, P., (2020) *Forgotten Peoples of the Ancient World*, Thames & Hudson, London

Murdoch, A., (2006) *Rome's Greatest Defeat, Massacre in the Teutoburg Forest*, The History Press, Stroud

Southern, P., (2001) *The Roman Empire from Severus to Constantine*, Routledge, Abingdon

Swain, S., Harrison, S. & Elsner, J., (2007) *Severan Culture*, Cambridge University Press, Cambridge

Syvänne, I., (2017) *Caracalla, A Military Biography*, Pen & Sword Military, Barnsley